Fetch the key facts with CGP!

Quick question — have you memorised the facts in CGP's
Knowledge Organiser for OCR GCSE Computer Science?

You have? Great! Now you can use this Knowledge Retriever
to check you've really got everything stuck in your brain.

There are retrieval quizzes for each topic, plus mixed quiz questions
to make extra sure you've really remembered all the vital facts. Enjoy.

CGP — still the best! ☺

Our sole aim here at CGP is to produce the highest quality books —
carefully written, immaculately presented and dangerously close to being funny.

Then we work our socks off to get them out to you
— at the cheapest possible prices.

Contents

Section Six — Programming

Section Seven — Design, Testing and IDEs

Published by CGP.
Based on the classic CGP style created by Richard Parsons.

Editors: Martha Bozic, Sammy El-Bahrawy, Shaun Harrogate, Andy Hurst.

With thanks to Michael Bushell for the proofreading.
With thanks to Alice Dent for the copyright research.

ISBN: 978 1 78908 950 9

Exam Reference Language OCR April 2020. OCR maintains the current version of the Exam Reference Language and specification on the OCR website. You should always check for the latest version and any updates. (https://www.ocr.org.uk/qualifications/gcse/computer-science-j277-from-2020/)

Printed by Elanders Ltd, Newcastle upon Tyne.
Clipart from Corel®

How to Use This Book

Every page in this book has a matching page in the GCSE Computer Science **Knowledge Organiser**. Before using this book, try to **memorise** everything on a Knowledge Organiser page. Then follow these **seven steps** to see how much knowledge you're able to retrieve...

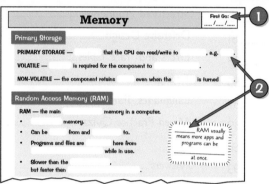

1 In this book, there are two versions of each page. Find the **'First Go'** of the page you've tried to memorise, and write the **date** at the top.

2 Use what you've learned from the Knowledge Organiser to **fill in** any dotted lines or white spaces.

You may need to draw, complete or add labels to tables and diagrams too.

3 Use the Knowledge Organiser to **check your work**.
Use a **different colour pen** to write in anything you missed or that wasn't quite right. This lets you see clearly what you **know** and what you **don't know**.

4 After doing the First Go page, **wait a few days**. This is important because **spacing out** your retrieval practice helps you to remember things better.

5 Now do the **Second Go** page.

The Second Go page is harder — it has more things missing.

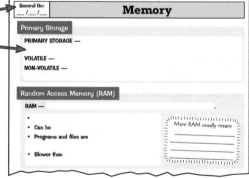

6 Again, check your work against the Knowledge Organiser and **correct it** with a different colour pen.
You should see some **improvement** between your first and second go.

7 **Wait** another few days, then try to reproduce any facts, methods, tables or diagrams from the Knowledge Organiser page on a **blank piece of paper**. You can also have a go at any **example questions**. If you can do this, you'll know you've **really learned it**.

There are also **Mixed Practice Quizzes** dotted throughout the book:
• The quizzes come in sets of four. They test a mix of content from the previous few pages.
• Do each quiz on a different day — write the date you do each one at the top of the quiz.
• Tick the questions you get right and record your score in the box at the end.
• Quiz questions marked with * have the answers given at back of the book.

Computer Systems and The CPU

First Go:
..... /..... /.....

Computer Systems

_____ — the physical stuff in a computer system, e.g. keyboard, CPU, etc.

SOFTWARE — _____,
e.g. operating system, games, web browser, etc.

EMBEDDED SYSTEMS — computers built into _____,
usually as _____. E.g. they could control:

Dishwashers   Microwaves   Sat navs

They're usually _____ to design,
to produce, and _____ at their
task than general purpose systems.

> External pieces of hardware like a keyboard or mouse are called ....

Four Common CPU Components

CENTRAL PROCESSING UNIT (CPU) — where a computer processes all _____ and _____.

1. Control Unit (CU) — controls the flow of _____ in and out of the _____. Manages the _____, _____ and _____ of instructions.

2. Arithmetic Logic Unit (ALU) — _____ including addition, subtraction, multiplication and division. Also performs _____ and _____.

3. Cache — stores _____ data for quick access. _____ capacity and _____. There are three levels of cache memory:

   L1 ——— L2 ———⟶ L3

   Decreasing ...., increasing capacity

4. Registers — _____ hold _____ of data. They're extremely _____ to read/write to.

Three Factors Affecting CPU Performance

1. Number of cores — each core _____ independently, so more cores means _____ instructions can be carried out _____. Some software is designed to take advantage of _____.

2. _____ — the number of instructions a single _____ can carry out per second.

3. Cache size — a _____ CPU cache gives the CPU faster access to _____.

> Generally, CPUs with more cores, higher clock speeds and larger caches will have .... performance, but .... more.

| Second Go: ...../...../..... | # Computer Systems and The CPU |

Computer Systems

HARDWARE —

SOFTWARE —

EMBEDDED SYSTEMS —

. E.g. they could control:

Dishwashers ....

They're usually

, and

at their task than general purpose systems.

.... pieces of hardware like a keyboard or mouse are called ....

Four Common CPU Components

CENTRAL PROCESSING UNIT (CPU) —

1 Control Unit (CU) —

2 Arithmetic Logic Unit (ALU) —

3 Cache —

There are three levels of cache memory:

L1 ——————— L2 ———————▶ L3

Decreasing ...., increasing ....

4 Registers —

Three Factors Affecting CPU Performance

1 Number of cores —

Some software is designed to

2 Clock speed —

3 Cache size —

Generally, CPUs with ...., ... and .... will have .... performance, but .... more.

How The CPU Works

Von Neumann Architecture

In the Von Neumann architecture, _____ and _____ Device
_____ are both stored in the same memory.

Central Processing Unit (CPU)

_____

Program Counter (PC) — holds
the _____
of the instruction for each
_____ .

Registers

_____

_____ (MAR)
— holds any memory address
about to be used by _____ .
The address could point to
_____ or an _____ .

Accumulator — stores
intermediate results of
_____ in the _____ .

Memory Data Register (MDR)
— holds the actual _____ or
_____ , either
from memory or waiting to be
_____ to memory.

Arrows show flow of data.

_____ Device

_____ — holds program
instructions and data.

Fetch-Execute Cycle

The fetch-execute cycle
repeats continuously while the
_____ .

1 FETCH

• _____ copied from
the program counter to the _____ .
• Instruction copied from
_____ to the _____ .
• Program counter incremented to point
to _____ .

2 _____

• Instruction in the MDR decoded
by the _____ .
• Control unit prepares for next
step, e.g. by loading values
into the _____ or _____ .

3 EXECUTE
Decoded instruction carried out.
Examples of instructions:
• Load _____ from _____ .
• Write _____ to _____ .
• Do _____ or
operation (using the ALU).

Section One — Components of a Computer System

Second Go:
..... /..... /.....

How The CPU Works

Von Neumann Architecture

In the Von Neumann architecture,

Central Processing Unit (CPU)

Program Counter (PC) —

Memory Address Register (MAR) —

The address could point to

Accumulator —

Memory Data Register (MDR) —

Arrows show ....
....

Fetch-Execute Cycle

The fetch-execute cycle
while the
.

1
- Memory address
- Instruction
- Program counter

3
Decoded instruction carried out.
Examples of instructions:
-
-
-

2
- Instruction in the MDR
- Control unit prepares for next step, e.g.

Memory

Primary Storage

PRIMARY STORAGE — _____ that the CPU can read/write to _____, e.g. _____.

VOLATILE — _____ is required for the component to _____.

NON-VOLATILE — the component retains _____ even when the _____ is turned _____.

Random Access Memory (RAM)

RAM — the main _____ memory in a computer.

- _____ memory.
- Can be _____ from and _____ to.
- Programs and files are _____ here from _____ while in use.
- Slower than the _____, but faster than _____.

> .... RAM usually means more apps and programs can be
> .... at once.

Virtual Memory

RAM can fill up if _____ apps, or _____ apps, are running, so some data is moved to a location in _____ called virtual memory.

.... Data not being used by CPU → ....
....

This data is moved back to _____ when the _____ needs it. Data transfer is _____ on secondary storage, so this _____.

.... Data needed by CPU → ....
....

Read Only Memory (ROM)

ROM — the main _____ memory in a computer.

- _____ memory.
- Can only be _____, not written to.
- Small amount of memory built into the _____.
- Contains **BIOS** (_____) — instructions needed for the _____.

> ROM is read only, but it is possible to ....
> .... on a ROM chip.

Second Go:	
..... / ..... /	**Memory**

Primary Storage

PRIMARY STORAGE —

VOLATILE —
NON-VOLATILE —

Random Access Memory (RAM)

RAM —

-
- Can be
- Programs and files are

- Slower than

More RAM usually means
....
....
....

Virtual Memory

RAM can fill up if

so some data is moved to

....
....
....

This data is moved back to

Data transfer is

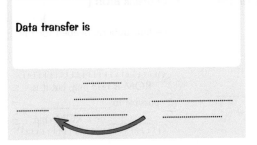

....
....
....

Read Only Memory (ROM)

ROM —

-
- Can only be

- Small amount of

- Contains

ROM is ...., but it
is possible to ....
.... on a ROM chip.

Mixed Practice Quizzes

That's it for the first few topics. Time to check what you've learned from p.3-8.
And remember, it's a quiz, not a test. Quizzes are fun. *Double thumbs up*

Quiz 1   Date: ...... / ...... / ......

1) What is the key feature of the Von Neumann architecture? ☑
2) Which CPU component controls the flow of data in and out of the CPU? ☑
3) Define the term 'primary storage'. ☑
4) What is the function of the accumulator? ☑
5) Which is faster for the CPU to access: RAM or secondary storage? ☑
6) Are keyboards and CPUs examples of hardware or software? ☑
7) When is virtual memory used? ☑
8) What term describes the number of instructions
   that a single processor core can carry out per second? ☑
9) What is ROM? ☑
10) Name the three stages of the fetch-execute cycle. ☑

Total: [   ]

Quiz 2   Date: ...... / ...... / ......

1) What happens during the 'fetch' stage of the fetch-execute cycle? ☑
2) What name is given to external hardware like a mouse and keyboard? ☑
3) What is software? ☑
4) What would be the benefit of adding more RAM to a computer? ☑
5) What kind of memory keeps its data without power? ☑
6) What do MDR and MAR stand for? ☑
7) Give one difference between Level 1 cache memory
   and Level 3 cache memory. ☑
8) Why might the use of virtual memory slow a computer's performance? ☑
9) Where is a ROM chip typically found in a computer? ☑
10) Will a CPU with multiple cores always perform better
    than one with a single core? Explain your answer. ☑

Total: [   ]

Mixed Practice Quizzes

Quiz 3 Date: ...... / ...... / ......

1) What does the CPU do?
2) True or false? The fetch-execute cycle only stops when the computer is turned off.
3) What does RAM stand for?
4) Which CPU component is the accumulator found in?
5) What does BIOS stand for?
6) Name three devices that contain embedded systems.
7) What is volatile memory?
8) What is the function of the ALU?
9) What is the purpose of registers inside the CPU?
10) Give two examples of instructions that may be carried out in the 'execute' stage of the fetch-execute cycle.

Total:

Quiz 4 Date: ...... / ...... / ......

1) Give three factors that affect CPU performance.
2) What is the function of the program counter?
3) Give two differences between RAM and ROM.
4) Give three examples of computer software.
5) What is an exception to the read only function of a ROM chip?
6) What is the function of the memory data register?
7) Will a CPU with a higher clock speed always perform better than one with a lower clock speed? Explain your answer.
8) How might increasing cache size improve CPU performance?
9) True or false? The CPU accesses virtual memory directly.
10) What are three advantages embedded systems have over general purpose systems?

Total:

Secondary Storage

Two Types of Internal Storage

SECONDARY STORAGE —
_____ storage
where programs and data are
_____.

1 _____ (HDDs)
- _____ parts.
- Store data
  on metal disks.
- Can be _____.

2 _____ (SSDs)
- No _____ parts.
- Use _____ memory for
  _____ read/write times.
- Usually _____.

Four Types of External Storage

1 Flash drives & memory cards
— _____ storage
used to expand the _____
of small devices.

2 _____ discs — e.g. CDs.
Can be read-only, _____
or _____.

3 _____ — used
by organisations to store
_____ amounts of data.

4 External HDDs & SSDs
— _____ versions
of internal storage. Often
used for _____.

Comparing Storage Types

_____   Memory Card   _____   HDD   SSD

Slow ——————— **Average Read/Write Speed** ——————→ Fast

Optical Disc   Memory Card   _____   _____   Magnetic Tape

Low ——————— **Average Capacity** ——————→ High

_____   Optical Disc   HDD   _____

Cheap ——————— **Average Cost (per GB)** ——————→ Expensive

	Internal HDD	Internal SSD	Memory Card	Optical Disc	Magnetic Tape
Portability	Low	___	High	High	___
Durability and Reliability	Damaged by _____. _____ read/write life.	Limited rewrites.	Shock resistant. _____	_____ Limited rewrites. Suitable _____ term storage.	Damaged by _____, _____ and magnets. Suitable _____ term storage.

| Second Go: ...../...../..... | **Secondary Storage** |

Two Types of Internal Storage

SECONDARY STORAGE —

1 _____ (HDDs)
-
-

-

2 _____ (SSDs)
-
-

-

Four Types of External Storage

1 Flash drives & memory cards —

2 Optical discs —

3 Magnetic tape —

4 External HDDs & SSDs —

Comparing Storage Types

Slow   **Average Read/Write Speed**   Fast →

Low   **Average Capacity**   High →

Cheap   **Average Cost (per GB)**   Expensive →

	Internal HDD	Internal SSD	Memory Card	Optical Disc	Magnetic Tape
Portability					
Durability and Reliability					

System Software — The OS

First Go:
..... /..... /.....

Five Functions of an Operating System (OS)

Function	Features
1 Peripheral management and drivers	• Communicates with internal _____, and _____ connected to the system, using _____. • Chooses _____ for connected hardware on startup. • Installs drivers for new _____ and _____ drivers automatically.
2 Providing a user interface	Allows users to _____ with a computer. Different _____ are designed for different _____: • _____ (GUIs) have windows, icons, menus and pointers. Designed for _____ users. • Command-Line Interfaces are _____ and use fewer _____ than GUIs. Used by advanced users.
3 Memory management and multitasking *These all help the CPU to multitask.*	• Moves _____ to main memory when in use and _____ it when it's no longer needed. • Allocates _____ so apps don't overwrite or interfere with each other. • Divides _____ between tasks to complete them _____. • Uses _____ buffers to _____ until other components or _____ are ready.
4 File and disk management	• Organises files into a _____ structure of _____. • Deals with _____, _____, moving, editing and deleting files and folders. • Splits the _____ into sectors and decides where files are _____. • Maintains the hard disk with _____.
5 User management	• Controls which users, and how many users, can _____. • Grants users access to specific _____ and resources — e.g. their own personal _____ and _____, but not that of _____. • Uses _____ to prevent access for other users — e.g. _____ or _____ protection.

Section One — Components of a Computer System

| Second Go:
..... / ..... / ..... | # System Software — The OS |

Five Functions of an Operating System (OS)

Function	Features
1 Peripheral management and drivers	• Communicates with • Chooses • Installs
2 Providing a user interface	Allows users to • Graphical User Interfaces (GUIs) have • Command-Line Interfaces are
3 Memory management and multitasking |||||||||||||/ These all help the CPU to multitask. /|||||||||||\	• Moves • Allocates • Divides • Uses
4 File and disk management	• Organises files into • Deals with • Splits the • Maintains
5 User management	• Controls • Grants users • Uses anti-theft measures to

Section One — Components of a Computer System   ☑ ☑ ☑

System Software — Utilities

Defragmentation Software

UTILITY SOFTWARE — software designed to [____] [____] a computer system.

Defragmentation software reorganises a [____] by putting related [____] back together. This speeds up [____] as the read/write head no longer has to [____] as much.

[____] don't need to be defragmented, they can access fragmented files [____]

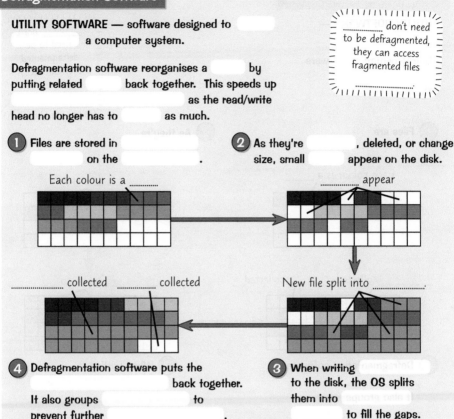

① Files are stored in [____] [____] on the [____].

Each colour is a [____]

② As they're [____], deleted, or change size, small [____] appear on the disk.

[____] appear

[____] collected   [____] collected

New file split into [____]

④ **Defragmentation software puts the** [____] **back together.** It also groups [____] to prevent further [____].

③ **When writing** [____] **to the disk, the OS splits them into** [____] **to fill the gaps.**

Compression Software

- [____] size of files by permanently or temporarily [____] from them.

- Compressed files take up [____] disk space and are [____] to upload and download.

- Compressed files need to be [____] before they can be used.

Encryption Software

- Scrambles ([____]) data to stop third-parties from [____].

- To [____] it back to its original form, a special '[____]' is needed.

- Only the computers of [____] have the [____], so stolen encrypted data is still [____].

- Strong encryption makes it almost impossible to find the key through [____].

Section One — Components of a Computer System

Second Go:
..... / ..... / .....

System Software — Utilities

Defragmentation Software

UTILITY SOFTWARE —

Defragmentation software

This speeds up

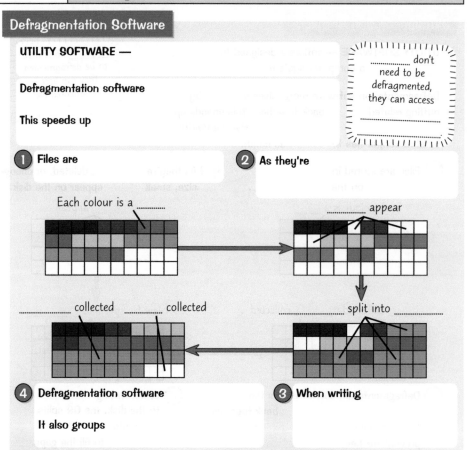

.... don't need to be defragmented, they can access ....

Each colour is a ....

1️⃣ Files are

2️⃣ As they're

.... appear

.... collected   .... collected

.... split into ....

4️⃣ **Defragmentation software**

It also groups

3️⃣ **When writing**

Compression Software

- **Reduces**

- **Compressed files take up**

- **Compressed files need to be**

Encryption Software

- **Scrambles (encrypts)**

- **To decrypt it back**

- **Only the computers of**

- **Strong encryption makes it almost impossible to**

Mixed Practice Quizzes

That's three more topics in your primary storage. Have a go at these questions to see how much data you've managed to read/write over p.11-16.

Quiz 1   Date: ...... / ...... / ......

1) What is disk fragmentation?

2) Name two types of internal secondary storage.

3) True or false? The operating system maintains the hard disk with utility software.

4) How does defragmentation speed up reading/writing files?

5) Give one drawback of using optical discs to store backups.

6) Give five things that the operating system helps to manage.

7) What is encryption software used for?

8) Which secondary storage type has the fastest read/write speed?

9) Describe two ways in which an operating system helps the CPU to multitask.

10) Why are memory cards often used in digital cameras and smartphones?

Total:

Quiz 2   Date: ...... / ...... / ......

1) What do drivers allow the operating system to do?

2) Name four types of external storage.

3) What is utility software?

4) What controls the number of users that can access a computer system?

5) When programs are not in use, are they kept in primary or secondary storage?

6) If encrypted data is stolen, why is it still secure?

7) How does an operating system allow users to interact with a computer?

8) How do HDDs and SSDs generally compare in terms of their cost per GB?

9) True or false? Fragmentation has the same effect on both HDDs and SSDs.

10) How does an operating system prevent applications from interfering with each other?

Total:

18

Mixed Practice Quizzes

Quiz 3   Date: ...... / ...... / ......

1) True or false? Secondary storage is volatile.
2) Which type of user interface is commonly used by everyday users?
3) Why do data gaps appear on a hard disk?
4) Which storage type would be more suitable as an everyday portable back up: memory cards or optical discs? Why is this?
5) Give two ways that the operating system manages users.
6) How does compression software work?
7) When is magnetic tape commonly used?
8) What does the operating system do when new peripherals are connected?
9) What is needed to decrypt encrypted data?
10) Which are more durable: HDDs or SSDs? Why is this?

Total:

Quiz 4   Date: ...... / ...... / ......

1) How does the operating system help to keep user accounts secure?
2) What does defragmentation software do to prevent further fragmentation?
3) Order the following from lowest to highest average capacity: SSDs, HDDs, memory cards, magnetic tape, optical discs.
4) What is the difference between GUIs and command-line interfaces?
5) Give two benefits of compressing files.
6) Are HDDs magnetic, optical or solid state storage?
7) How does the operating system help to organise files on a computer system?
8) What needs to be done to a compressed file before it can be used?
9) Give five things someone might consider when choosing an external storage device.
10) What does an operating system use memory buffers for?

Total:

Number Systems

First Go:
..... / ..... / .....

Three Important Number Systems

1 DENARY (BASE ___)
- ___ digits: _____
- Place values are powers of ___ (100s, 10s, 1s).

2 BINARY (BASE ___)
- ___ digits: _____
- Place values are powers of ___ (8s, 4s, 2s, 1s).

3 HEXADECIMAL (BASE ___)
- ___ digits: _____
  _____
- Place values are powers of ___ (256s, 16s, 1s).

Programmers like hex because the numbers are _____ and easy to _____, and can be easily converted to _____.

Denary	Binary	Hex
0		0
1		1
2	0010	2
3	0011	3
4	0100	
5	0101	

Denary	Binary	Hex
6	0110	6
7		7
8	1000	8
9	1001	
10	1010	

Denary	Binary	Hex
	1011	
	1100	C
13	1101	D
14	1110	E
15		

Converting Binary to Denary...

1 Put the number in a _____ place value table.

2 Add up the _____ in columns where there's a ___.

EXAMPLE

Convert 10011100 from binary to denary.

1
128		32	16	8		2	1
1	0	0	1	1	1	0	0

2 128 + 16 + ___ + ___ = ___

...and Denary to Binary

1 Draw a _____ place value table.

2 Keep _____ the biggest place values you can until you're left with ___.

3 If you _____ a place value, put a ___ in that column, otherwise put a ___.

EXAMPLE

Convert 170 from denary to binary.

1
128		16	8	4	2	1

2 170 − 128 = ___   10 − ___ = 2
   ___ − 32 = 10   ___ − ___ = 0

3
128		16	8	4	2	1
1	0	1	0		1	0

Second Go: ..... / ..... /	# Number Systems

Three Important Number Systems

1 DENARY ( )
•
• Place values

2 BINARY ( )
•
• Place values

3 HEXADECIMAL ( )
•

• Place values

Programmers like hex because the numbers are ....
....
....

Denary	Binary	Hex
0		
1		
2		
3		
4		
5		

Denary	Binary	Hex
6		
7		
8		
9		
10		

Denary	Binary	Hex
11		
12		
13		
14		
15		

Converting Binary to Denary...

1 Put the number in a

2 Add up the

EXAMPLE

Convert 10011100 from binary to denary.

1

1	0	0	1	1	1	0	0

2

...and Denary to Binary

1 Draw a

2 Keep subtracting

3 If you subtracted a place value,

EXAMPLE

Convert 170 from denary to binary.

1

2 170 – <u>128</u> =

3

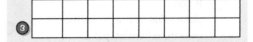

Converting Hexadecimal

Converting Hex to Denary...

1 Put the number in a ____ place value table.

2 Multiply (in denary) the ____ in each ____.

3 Add up ____.

EXAMPLE

Convert A2 from hexadecimal to denary.

1
16	1

2 A in hex is 10 in denary, so: 10 × 16 = ____
2 × 1 = ____

3 A2 is ____ + ____ = ____ in denary.

...and Denary to Hex

1 Divide by ____ to get a quotient and a ____.

2 Convert each value to ____.

3 The quotient is the ____ digit and the ____ is the ____.

EXAMPLE

Convert 43 from denary to hexadecimal.

1 43 ÷ ____ = ____ remainder ____

2 2 in denary is ____ in hex. 11 in denary is ____ in hex.

3 43 is ____ in hexadecimal.

Converting Binary to Hex...

1 Put the number in a table that repeats ____ ...
Add ____ to the front so that it splits into ____.

2 For each ____, add up the place values in columns where there's a ____, and convert into ____.

EXAMPLE

Convert 110 1101 from binary to hex.

1
8			1		4	2	
O	1	1	O	1	1	O	1

2 ____ + ____ = 6   8 + ____ + ____ = 13
6 in denary is ____ in hex. 13 in denary is ____ in hex.
So 110 1101 is ____ in hexadecimal.

...and Hex to Binary

1 Convert each ____ digit into a ____ binary number.

2 Put the ____ together.

EXAMPLE

Convert E4 from hexadecimal to binary.

1 E in hex is ____ in denary, which is ____ in binary.
4 in hex is ____ in denary, which is ____ in binary.

2 So E4 is ____ in binary.

Section Two — Data Representation

| Second Go: ...../...../..... | **Converting Hexadecimal** |

Converting Hex to Denary...

1. Put the number in a
2. Multiply (in denary)
3. Add up

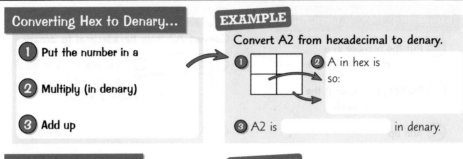

EXAMPLE

Convert A2 from hexadecimal to denary.

1. [table]
2. A in hex is
   so:
3. A2 is _____ in denary.

...and Denary to Hex

1. Divide by
2. Convert
3. The quotient is

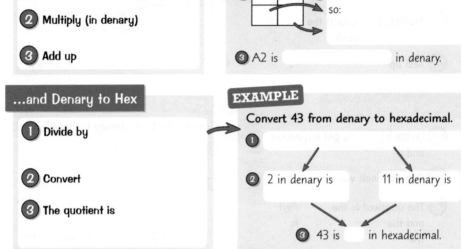

EXAMPLE

Convert 43 from denary to hexadecimal.

1.
2. 2 in denary is   11 in denary is
3. 43 is [ ] in hexadecimal.

Converting Binary to Hex...

1. Put the number in a table that repeats
2. For each nibble,

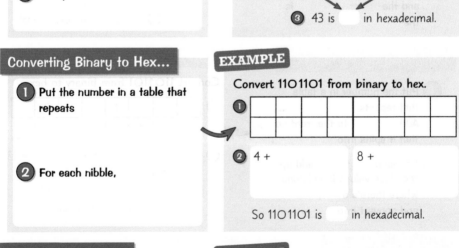

EXAMPLE

Convert 1101101 from binary to hex.

1. [table]
2. 4 +   8 +

So 1101101 is [ ] in hexadecimal.

...and Hex to Binary

1. Convert
2. Put the

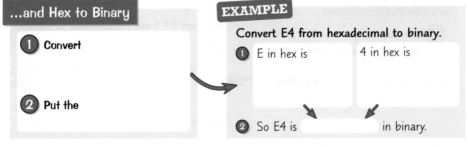

EXAMPLE

Convert E4 from hexadecimal to binary.

1. E in hex is   4 in hex is
2. So E4 is _____ in binary.

Section Two — Data Representation

Using Binary

Binary Addition

To add binary numbers, use [_____].

Remember the four simple rules:

1. 0 + 0 = [__]
2. 0 + 1 = [__]
3. 1 + 1 = [__] (carry a [__])
4. 1 + 1 + 1 = [__] (carry a [__])

EXAMPLE

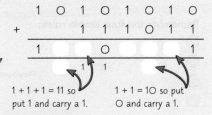

Work out 10101010 + 111011.

```
    1  0  1  0  1  0  1  0
  +       1  1  1  0  1  1
 ─────────────────────────
    1        0           1
          1  1
```

1 + 1 + 1 = 11 so put 1 and carry a 1.   1 + 1 = 10 so put 0 and carry a 1.

Binary Shifts

BINARY SHIFT — move every [____] in a number [____] or [____] a certain number of [____].

Gaps at the [____] or [____] of the number are filled in with [__].

Left shifts [_____].
For every place shifted left, the number is [_____].

Right shifts [_____].
For every place shifted right, the number is [_____].

Overflow Errors

OVERFLOW ERROR — when binary [_____] gives a result that requires more [____] than the CPU is [____].

Overflow errors can lead to a loss of [____] or [____].

- In binary addition, two [____] numbers might add to give a [____] number. If the CPU expects an [____] answer then bits will be [____].
- Left shifts can cause the [____] significant bits to be [____].
- Right shifts can cause the [____] significant bits to be [____].

The most significant bit is the ....-most bit.
The least significant bit is the ....-most bit.

EXAMPLE

Describe the effect of a 2-place left shift on 01011101.

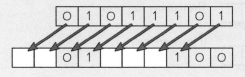

```
  0  1  0  1  1  1  0  1
        0  1        1  0  0
```

The number has been [____] twice, or multiplied by [__] = 4.

If there are only [____] available to store the result, then the two [____] significant bits will [_____].

Second Go:
...... / ...... / ......

Using Binary

Binary Addition

To add

Remember the four simple rules:

①
②
③
④

EXAMPLE

Work out 10101010 + 111011.

Binary Shifts

BINARY SHIFT —

Gaps at the

Left shifts

Right shifts

Overflow Errors

OVERFLOW ERROR —

Overflow errors can lead to

• In binary addition,

   If the CPU expects an

• Left shifts can cause

• Right shifts can cause

The most significant bit is the .... bit.
The least significant bit is the .... bit.

EXAMPLE

Describe the effect of a 2-place left shift on 01011101.

The number has been

If there are only

Mixed Practice Quizzes

You know the drill by now. More topics = more questions to see what's gone in and what's spilled out as an overflow error. Try these questions covering p.19-24.

Quiz 1 Date: ...... / ...... / ......

1) Name three different number systems.
2) What number do you divide by when converting denary to hex?
3) Will a left shift or a right shift cause the most significant bits to be lost?
4) Outline how to convert a binary number to denary.
5) How many different numbers can be represented with 4 bits?
6) Define the term 'overflow error'. What can they lead to?
7)* Convert F4 from hex to denary.
8) What is the denary number 5 in binary?
9)* What is 01001011 + 01111001?
   Give your answer as an 8-bit binary number.
10)*Convert 10111011 from binary to denary.

Total:

Quiz 2 Date: ...... / ...... / ......

1) True or false? Binary is base 1.
2) What is a binary shift?
3) How would you convert denary to binary using a place value table?
4) How do the quotient and the remainder form a hexadecimal number when converting denary to hex?
5)* Convert 10001001 from binary to denary.
6) Describe how overflow errors can occur from binary addition.
7) What is the binary number 1100 in denary?
8) Describe the effect of a 3-place binary right shift.
9)* Convert 118 from denary to hex.
10)*Perform a 2-place left shift on the binary number 00100111.
   Give your answer as an 8-bit binary number.

Total:

Mixed Practice Quizzes

Date: ...... / ...... / ......

1) What are the four simple rules of binary addition?
2) What does 'base 2' mean?
3)* Convert 10100111 from binary to hex.
4) What is the difference between a left and right binary shift?
5) What is the denary number 14 in hex?
6) When converting binary to hex,
   what should you split the binary number into?
7)* Convert 162 from denary to binary.
8) List the 16 digits used in hexadecimal.
9)* What is 100101 + 1100000?
   Give your answer as an 8-bit binary number.
10) True or false? A single right shift multiplies a binary number by 2.

Total:

Quiz 4   Date: ...... / ...... / ......

1) When performing a binary shift are gaps at
   the beginning and end filled with 0s or 1s?
2) Outline the steps you would take to convert a number from hex to denary.
3) What is the binary number 1010 in hex?
4) What is meant by 'the most significant bit'?
5)* Perform a 3-place right shift on the binary number 10100100.
   Give your answer as an 8-bit binary number.
6) Explain why programmers might prefer using hex numbers.
7)* Convert B9 from hex to binary.
8) In denary, place values are powers of which number?
9)* Convert 237 from denary to binary.
10) True or false? Hexadecimal is base 12.

Total:

Units and Compression

Eight Units of Data Size

Computers can only store and process ....

They use ...... and ...... to represent the .... of electricity — a ..... shows that electricity ...., and a ...... shows that it ....

Each ...... or ...... in binary data is a .... (<u>bi</u>nary di<u>git</u>). The .... of a file is the number of ...... and ...... that make up its data.

	Name	Size
①	Bit (b)	
②		4 bits
③	Byte (B)	
④	Kilobyte (kB)	
⑤	(MB)	1000 kilobytes
⑥	(GB)	1000 megabytes
⑦	Terabyte (TB)	
⑧	Petabyte (PB)	

Traditionally, each unit is defined to be .... times bigger than the previous one.

Data Compression

DATA COMPRESSION — making file sizes [   ], while trying to stay as [   ] to the [   ] as possible.

Benefits of data compression:
• Compressed files use [   ] storage space.
• Streaming/downloading compressed files takes [   ] bandwidth.
• Some services like email have [   ] limits — compression can get a file [   ] the limit.

Two Types of Compression

① **LOSSY COMPRESSION** — [   ] removes data from the file.

② **LOSSLESS COMPRESSION** — [   ] removes data to [   ] the file, and [   ] it to its original state when [   ].

	Pros	Cons
Lossy	• [ ] reduction in file size, so they can be [ ] easier, and [ ] faster. • [ ] — lots of software can read lossy files.	• Loses [ ] — the file can't be turned back into [ ]. • Can't be used on [ ]. • Reduction in [ ].
Lossless	• No reduction in [ ]. • File can be turned back into [ ]. • Can be used on [ ].	• Comparatively small reduction in [ ] — lossless files take up more [ ] than lossy files.

Section Two — Data Representation

Units and Compression

Eight Units of Data Size

Computers can only ....
....

They use 1s and 0s to represent the

.... —

a .... shows that ....
........................., and a .... shows that

....

Each 1 or 0 in binary data is ....
(..............................). The size of a file
is the ....
....

Name	Size
① Bit (b)	
②	
③ (B)	
④ (kB)	
⑤ (MB)	
⑥ (GB)	
⑦ (TB)	
⑧ (PB)	

Traditionally, each unit is defined to be .... than the previous one.

Data Compression

DATA COMPRESSION —

Benefits of data compression:
• Compressed files use
• Streaming/downloading

• Some services like email

Two Types of Compression

① LOSSY COMPRESSION —

② LOSSLESS COMPRESSION —

	Pros	Cons
Lossy	• Big	• Loses
	• Commonly used —	• Can't be used on
		• Reduction in
Lossless	• No reduction	• Comparatively small
	• File can be	
	• Can be used on	

Characters

Character Sets

CHARACTERS — _____ and _____ letters, the _____,
and _____ like ?, + and £. Used to make _____ and _____.

CHARACTER SETS — collections of _____ that a computer
recognises from their _____, used to
convert _____ to _____ and vice versa.

_____ on _____ ⟶ _____ sent to computer ⟶ Computer _____ using character set

keyboard

Two Important Character Sets

1 ASCII

- Each character is given a _____ binary code —
  so ASCII can represent _____ different characters.
- An extra _____ (0) is added to the start of each
  _____ so each character uses _____.
- The _____ for numbers and letters are _____
  (A comes before B comes before C...).

Character	Binary	Denary
A	01000001	65
B		66
C	01000011	67
a	01100001	97
b		98
c	01100011	99

As the codes are
...................., you
can work out the
code for one letter,
given the code of
another.

2 UNICODE®

- Covers _____ major _____, including ones that use
  different _____, like Greek, Russian and Chinese.
- Uses multiple _____ for each _____.
- The first _____ characters in Unicode® are the same as _____.

Text File Sizes

File size (in _____) = number of _____ × number of _____

EXAMPLE

How many bits would be needed to store "I'm a string, store me!" in 8-bit ASCII?

Count the number of .... ⟶ I'm a string, store me!

5   10   20

Use the formula. ⟶ File size = 8 × _____ = _____ bits

Remember to
count characters
like ....
and ....

 ✓ ✓ ✓

Section Two — Data Representation

Second Go: ..... / ..... /	**Characters**

Character Sets

CHARACTERS —

Used to make

CHARACTER SETS — collections of

Button ➡ [ ] ➡ Computer

Two Important Character Sets

1 ASCII

• Each character is given

• An extra bit (0)

• The codes

Character	Binary	Denary
A	01000001	65
B		66
C		67
a	01100001	97
b		98
c		99

As the codes are ...., you can work out the code for ...., given the ....

2 Unicode®

• Covers

• Uses multiple

• The first

Text File Sizes

[ ] = [ ] × [ ]

EXAMPLE

How many bits would be needed to store "I'm a string, store me!" in 8-bit ASCII?

Count the
....
....

➡ [ ]

Remember to count characters like .... and ....

Use the formula. ➡ File size =

Storing Images

Representing Images

BITMAP — a type of _____ made up of lots of _____, called _____.
The colour of each _____ is stored using a _____.

IMAGE RESOLUTION — the number of _____ in a bitmap image.
Often given as '_____ × _____'.

COLOUR DEPTH — the number of _____ used to represent each _____.

The number of _____ that can be used for a
given _____ follows this formula:

Total number of _____ = _____ (where n = _____)

EXAMPLE

Colour depth = 2 bits

- Number of _____ = _____ = _____
- In this example,
  00 → white, 01 → light grey,
  10 → dark grey, 11 → black.

.....	01	10	00
01	10	.....	10
.....	00	10	.....
.....	10	01	11

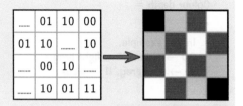

Image File Sizes

Use this formula to calculate file size:

File size (in _____)
= image _____ × colour _____
= width × _____ × colour _____

Increasing the image _____ or
colour _____ will usually give a higher
_____ image, but a _____ file size.

EXAMPLE

Calculate the size in kB of a
100 × 100 pixel image with
a colour depth of 16 bits.

File size = 100 × _____ × _____
= _____ bits

_____ bits
= _____ ÷ _____ = 20 000 bytes
= 20 000 ÷ _____ = _____ kB

Metadata

METADATA — data stored in a file which
contains _____ about
the _____. Helps the computer to
_____ the image on screen from
the _____ in each pixel.

Examples of metadata

- height & _____
- colour _____
- _____
- file _____
- _____ created
- date last _____

Second Go:
..... / ..... / .....

Storing Images

Representing Images

BITMAP — a type of

IMAGE RESOLUTION — the number of

COLOUR DEPTH — the number of

The ⬚⬚⬚ that can be used for
a given ⬚⬚⬚ follows this formula:

⬚⬚⬚ = ⬚⬚⬚

EXAMPLE

Colour depth = ⬚⬚⬚

• ⬚⬚⬚

• In this example,
00 → white, 01 → light grey,
10 → dark grey, 11 → black.

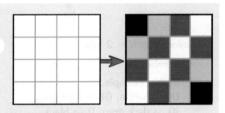

Image File Sizes

Use this formula to calculate file size:
File size (⬚⬚⬚)

= ⬚⬚⬚ × ⬚⬚⬚

= ⬚⬚⬚ × ⬚⬚⬚ × ⬚⬚⬚

Increasing the

EXAMPLE

Calculate the size in kB of a
100 × 100 pixel image with
a colour depth of 16 bits.

File size =

Metadata

METADATA —

Helps the computer to

Examples of metadata
•
•
•
•
•

Storing Sound

Key Definitions

SAMPLING	Converting an _____ sound wave into _____ _____ that can be read and stored by a _____ .
SAMPLE RATE	The number of _____ taken per _____ . Usually measured in _____ . Also called sampling _____
BIT DEPTH	The number of _____ available for each _____ .

Sound Sampling Process

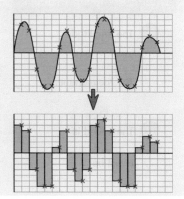

1 The _____ of the sound wave is measured at _____ , based on the _____ rate.
The measurements are only able to take certain _____ , based on the _____ .

2 The sound is _____ based on the _____ taken. It will be a _____ to the analogue wave, but will have lost some _____ .

Sound File Sizes

$$\text{File size (in bits)} = \underline{\hspace{3cm}} \text{(in Hz)} \times \underline{\hspace{3cm}} \times \text{length (in seconds)}$$

A higher _____ or _____ will give a higher _____ sound file, but will increase the _____ .

EXAMPLE

Calculate the file size in MB of a 50 second audio recording with a sample rate of 40 kHz and a bit depth of 8 bits.

1 kHz = _____   40 kHz = _____

Use the formula.   File size = _____ × 8 × 50 = _____ bits

Convert from bits to MB.   _____ bits = _____ bytes

= _____ kB = _____ MB

            Section Two — Data Representation

Second Go: ...../...../.....	**Storing Sound**

Key Definitions

SAMPLING	Converting an
SAMPLE RATE	The number of
	Also called
BIT DEPTH	The number of

Sound Sampling Process

1 The amplitude

The measurements

2 The sound is

It will be

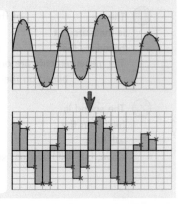

Sound File Sizes

[ ] = [ ] × [ ] × [ ]

A higher

EXAMPLE

Calculate the file size in MB of a 50 second audio recording with a sample rate of 40 kHz and a bit depth of 8 bits.

1 kHz = [ ]   40 kHz = [ ]

Use the formula.

Convert from bits to MB.

Mixed Practice Quizzes

Right, that's a few more topics ticked off the list. See what you can remember from p.27-34 by giving these questions a go. Then have a biscuit or something.

Quiz 1   Date: ...... / ...... / ......

1) Define the term 'data compression'.

2) What are character sets and what are they used for?

3) Which is bigger, a megabyte or a gigabyte?

4) How is an analogue sound wave converted to a digital sound wave?

5)* How many bits would be needed to store "£1000? That's ridiculous!" in 8-bit ASCII?

6) True or false? Computers can only store and process binary data.

7) Define the term 'image resolution'.

8) What effect will increasing bit depth have on the size of a sound file?

9) Give two differences between ASCII and Unicode®.

10) What are three benefits of data compression?

Total:

Quiz 2   Date: ...... / ...... / ......

1) How many characters are in the ASCII character set? Why is this?

2) What is a bit?

3) What is the term for the number of bits available for each sound sample?

4)* In an image with a colour depth of 4 bits, how many unique colours can be used?

5) What is the formula for working out text file sizes (in bits)?

6)* What is the file size, in kB, of a 5 second audio file with a 40 kHz sample rate and a bit depth of 16 bits?

7) In terms of electricity flow, what do 1 and 0 represent?

8) Give six examples of metadata for an image.

9) Define the term 'character'.

10) Why might someone choose to use lossless compression over lossy?

Total:

Mixed Practice Quizzes

Quiz 3 Date: ...... / ...... / ......

1) What is a bitmap image?
2) What is a sample rate? What unit is it usually measured in?
3) How many bits are there in:
   a) a nibble?   b) a byte?   c)* a kilobyte?
4) Name two character sets.
5) What is the formula for calculating the file size of an image?
6) What is the key difference between lossy and lossless compression?
7)* In ASCII, 01000100 is the code for "D". What is the code for "F"?
8) How does a digitally recreated sound wave differ from the original analogue wave?
9) What two things could you increase to improve image quality? What drawback would doing this have?
10) True or false? Text files can be compressed using lossy compression.

Total:

Quiz 4 Date: ...... / ...... / ......

1) What is the term for the number of bits used to represent each pixel?
2) Define the term 'sampling'.
3) True or false? When calculating text file size, spaces count as characters.
4) What is the name of the unit with a size equivalent to 1000 terabytes?
5) What is metadata?
6) What is the formula for calculating the size of a sound file?
7)* What is the file size, in MB, of a 1000 × 1000 pixel image with a 24-bit colour depth?
8) True or false? The first 128 characters in Unicode® are the same as ASCII.
9)* An audio clip was recorded with a sample rate of 40 kHz and a bit depth of 8 bits. The sound file produced was 80 kB, how long (in seconds) was the clip?
10) Which type of compression will generally reduce a file size more?

Total:

Section Two — Data Representation

Types of Network

First Go:
..... /..... /.....

LANs — Local Area Networks

LANs cover _____ geographical areas at _____ — e.g. in businesses or schools.

LAN hardware is usually owned by _____.

They can be _____ or _____.

Users on a LAN can:

- Access and share _____ on the network.
- Share _____.
- Share an _____ connection.
- Log in from _____ on the network.
- Roll out _____ and _____ updates to all computers at once.

Typical devices on a LAN

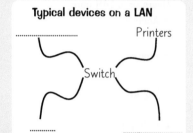

Printers

Switch

WANs — Wide Area Networks

WANs connect LANs in _____ geographical locations.

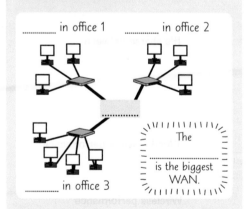

.... in office 1   .... in office 2

The .... is the biggest WAN.

.... in office 3

Organisations hire _____ (e.g. _____ lines or _____ links) from telecommunications companies, who _____ and _____ the WAN.

More _____ to set up than LANs.

Network Performance

BANDWIDTH — amount of _____ that can be _____ in a given time.

It's shared between _____ on a _____. _____ bandwidth, _____ use (e.g. streaming video), or _____ devices can slow a network.

Wired network performance can depend on the _____ _____ used.

Wireless performance depends on _____ _____, which is affected by:

- _____ of the device
- _____ from other networks
- _____

Types of Network

LANs — Local Area Networks

LANs cover

LAN hardware is
They can be

Users on a **LAN** can:
• Access

• Share

• Share

• Log in

• Roll out

Typical devices on a LAN

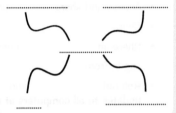

....

....

....

WANs — Wide Area Networks

WANs connect

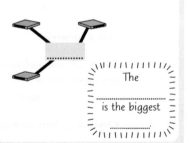

The
....
is the biggest
....

Organisations hire

More .... **to set up than LANs.**

Network Performance

BANDWIDTH —

It's shared between

Wired network performance

Wireless performance

•

•

•

Network Hardware

First Go:
..... /..... /.....

Five Pieces of Network Hardware

Hardware	Function
1 Network Interface Controller (NIC)	Allows devices to ⬚ — usually built into the ⬚.
2 Switch	⬚ and transmits data between devices on a ⬚ using ⬚.
3 Transmission Media	⬚ or wireless ⬚ that allow data transmission between devices.
4 Wireless Access Point (WAP)	Allows devices to ⬚ wirelessly. Similar to a ⬚.
5 Router	Transmits data between ⬚ by directing data as '⬚' to their destination.	Most 'routers' are a ...., ... and .... all in one.

Wired Networks

Three cables to connect devices on an ⬚ (wired) network:

1 ⬚ — copper wires twisted together in ⬚ to reduce ⬚ interference.

2 Coaxial — a single ⬚ wire surrounded by insulation and ⬚ mesh to shield from interference.

3 Fibre optic — transmits data as ⬚. Can send data over ⬚ with little ⬚. High performance but ⬚.

Wired networks tend to be ⬚ and ⬚ than wireless networks.

Wireless Networks

Radio waves transmit data between ⬚ on ⬚ networks.

Two common wireless technologies:

1 Bluetooth® — direct connection between ⬚ devices to ⬚ data. ⬚ bandwidth.

Max range

2 ⬚ — can connect ⬚ to a **LAN** at once. ⬚ bandwidth.

Max range ⬚

Wireless networks tend to be ⬚ and ⬚ than wired networks.

 ✓ ✓ ☺ ✓

Second Go:
..... / ..... / .....

Network Hardware

Five Pieces of Network Hardware

Hardware	Function
① Network Interface Controller (NIC)	
② Switch	Receives and transmits
③ Transmission Media	
④ Wireless Access Point (WAP)	Allows devices to
⑤ Router	Transmits data between

Most 'routers' are a ...., ... and .... all in one.

Wired Networks

Three cables to connect devices on

① Twisted pair —

② Coaxial —

③ Fibre optic —

Wired networks tend to be

Wireless Networks

Radio waves transmit

Two common wireless technologies:

①

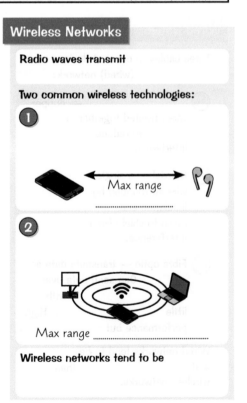

Max range ....

②

Max range ....

Wireless networks tend to be

  ☑ ☑ ☑

Networks and Topologies

Client-Server Networks

Files, software, user profiles and passwords are all stored _____ on the _____. _____ sends a request to the _____. _____ processes the request and _____.

PROS
- Easy _____ tracking — all stored centrally.
- _____ files and _____ software easily.
- Servers are _____ and always _____.
- Security — servers can request _____ or access levels before fulfilling _____.

CONS
- _____ to set up and maintain.
- If the server goes down all clients _____.
- Servers can get _____ with too many _____.

Peer-to-Peer Networks

Devices connect _____ — no server.

Files are stored on _____ and shared with others.

PROS
- Easy to _____ without expertise.
- No dependance on _____.

CONS
- _____ and _____ are complicated.
- Hard to _____ files — copying between _____ creates _____.
- Data could be lost if _____.

Star Topology

All devices connect to a central _____ or _____ that controls the network.

Star Topology

PROS
- Network unaffected if a device _____.
- Easy to _____ devices.
- _____ performance.

CONS
- Expensive for _____ networks.
- _____ is a single point of failure.

Mesh Topology

No _____ — data sent along fastest route from one _____ to _____.

.... Mesh   .... Mesh

PROS
- No _____ of failure.
- Add devices without _____.

CONS
- _____ for wired networks.
- _____ to maintain lots of connections.

Networks and Topologies

Client-Server Networks

Files, software, user profiles and passwords are

Client sends

Server processes

PROS
- Easy file tracking —
-
- Servers are
- Security —

CONS
-
- If the server goes down
- Servers can get

Peer-to-Peer Networks

Devices connect
Files are stored on

PROS
- Easy to
-

CONS
- Updates and
- Hard to track
- Data could be

Star Topology

All devices connect to

Star Topology

PROS
- Network
- Easy to
-

CONS
- Expensive for
- Switch is a single

Mesh Topology

No switch —

Full Mesh   Partial Mesh

PROS
- No single
- Add devices

CONS
- Expensive for
- Hard to

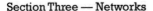

Mixed Practice Quizzes

What do you WANt? More quizzes? And WAN do you WANt it? Right now?
I hear you. Answer these questions to see what you've LANed over pages 37-42.

Quiz 1 Date: ...... / ...... / ......

1) What do LAN and WAN stand for?
2) What advantages do wired networks have over wireless networks?
3) How do client-server networks differ from peer-to-peer networks?
4) True or false? The Internet is an example of a WAN.
5) Name five pieces of network hardware.
6) What is a star topology?
7) Give three reasons why a network connection may be slow.
8) Name three cables that can connect devices on an Ethernet network.
9) What are the drawbacks of using a mesh topology?
10) What is the function of a router?

Total:

Quiz 2 Date: ...... / ...... / ......

1) What is transmission media?
2) How do LANs and WANs differ in terms of the area they cover?
3) What are the advantages of using client-server networks over peer-to-peer?
4) What do wireless networks use to transmit data between devices?
5) Who (usually) owns and manages a WAN?
6) How does a mesh topology differ from a star topology?
7) Which other pieces of network hardware do routers usually contain?
8) Name four typical devices that you'd find on a LAN.
9) What is the difference between a full and a partial mesh topology?
10) What advantages do wireless networks have over wired networks?

Total:

Mixed Practice Quizzes

1) What type of address does a switch use to receive and transmit data?
2) Give five benefits of using a LAN.
3) Why might someone choose to use a peer-to-peer network instead of a client-server one?
4) What is the difference between twisted pair and fibre optic cables?
5) Give one factor, unique to wired networks, that can affect network performance.
6) What are the network benefits of using a star topology?
7) Which piece of hardware do all devices on a LAN connect to?
8) Which is usually more expensive to set up, LANs or WANs?
9) How does a client-server network work?
10) True or false? Bluetooth® has a higher bandwidth than Wi-Fi®.

Total:

1) True or false? In a LAN, the hardware is usually hired from someone else.
2) Define the term 'bandwidth'.
3) What would happen to a network using a star topology if the switch fails?
4) Other than bandwidth, give two differences between Bluetooth® and Wi-Fi® networks.
5) Which piece of network hardware allows wireless network connection?
6) What are the main drawbacks of a peer-to-peer network?
7) What is the function of a network interface controller (NIC)?
8) What do fibre optic cables use to transmit data and how does this help with performance?
9) Name four things that may be stored centrally on the server of a client-server network.
10) What three factors can affect wireless signal quality on a network?

Total:

Network Protocols

Network Addressing

IP ADDRESSES — unique _____ - or _____ -bit identifiers given to devices when _____. E.g. 37.153.62.136

MAC ADDRESSES — unique _____ - or _____ -bit identifiers given to network devices _____. E.g. 98-81-55-CD-F2-2F

Protocols

NETWORK STANDARD — a set of agreed _____ for _____ and _____ that allows different _____ to make compatible products.

NETWORK COMMUNICATION PROTOCOL — rules for how devices _____, and how data is _____ and _____ across a network.

Transmission Control Protocol (TCP) — sets _____ for how devices _____ to a network. Splits and reassembles _____. Checks they're _____ and delivered.

Internet Protocol (IP) — directs _____ to their destination across a network.

Simple Mail Transfer Protocol (SMTP) — sends and transfers _____ between _____.

Post Office Protocol (POP) — retrieves _____ from a server. Server _____ the email after you _____ it.

Hyper Text Transfer Protocol (HTTP) — _____ use it to access websites and _____.

HTTP Secure (HTTPS) — _____ website information sent and received for _____.

File Transfer Protocol (FTP) — accesses, _____ and _____ files between devices on a _____.

Instant Messaging Access Protocol (IMAP) — retrieves _____ from a server. Server _____ it until you _____ it.

Network Layers

Network communication is divided by _____ into layers.

Each layer is _____. It serves the layer _____ it and depends on all the layers _____ it.

Benefits of network layers:
- Developers can each focus on _____ of the _____.
- Layers can be changed _____ others.
- Standards develop ensuring _____ between different pieces of _____ and _____.

Layer	Protocol
4	HTTP
3	TCP
2	IP
1	Ethernet

Network Protocols

Network Addressing

IP ADDRESSES —

E.g. 37.153.62.136

MAC ADDRESSES —

E.g. 98-81-55-CD-F2-2F

Protocols

NETWORK STANDARD —

NETWORK COMMUNICATION PROTOCOL —

Transmission Control Protocol (TCP) —

Internet Protocol (IP) —

Simple Mail Transfer Protocol (SMTP) —

Post Office Protocol (POP) —

Hyper Text Transfer Protocol (HTTP) —

HTTP Secure (HTTPS) —

File Transfer Protocol (FTP) —

Instant Messaging Access Protocol (IMAP) —

Network Layers

Network communication is
Each layer is

Benefits of network layers:
• Developers can each focus on
• Layers can be
• Standards develop ensuring

Layer	Protocol
4	HTTP
3	TCP
2	IP
1	Ethernet

Internet Services

The Internet

INTERNET — a worldwide collection of _____.

WORLD WIDE WEB — a collection of _____ hosted on _____. Accessed through the _____ protocol.

URLs — _____ used to access web servers and resources on them, e.g:

https://www.cgpbooks.co.uk/guestbook

Protocol .... Path to a file or page.
....

Domain Name Service (DNS)

A service made of many _____ _____ that store domain names and matching _____.

1. Browser sends _____ to _____.

2. _____ finds matching _____ address and sends it back to _____.

3. Browser requests _____ from the _____ at the IP address.

4. _____ processes the request and sends the _____ back.

Hosting and The Cloud

HOSTING — when a business uses its _____ to _____ for another organisation, e.g. hosting websites on _____ or files on _____.

THE CLOUD — _____ accessed over the _____ that offer a range of services including:

1. _____ and _____ data and files — users need less _____ on their own computer.

2. Running cloud _____ — users can access _____ without needing it on their own computer.

3. Providing increased _____ power — users don't need to have _____ in their computer.

Pros of the cloud	Cons of the cloud
• Access files from _____.	• Requires _____ connection.
• Easy to increase _____.	• Relies on host for _____ and _____.
• No need for _____ and the _____ to manage it.	• Stored data can be _____.
• Host provides _____ and _____.	• Unclear who has _____ of data.
• Automatic _____.	• _____ subscription fees.

 ☑ ☑ ☺ ☑

Second Go: ..... /..... /.....	# Internet Services

The Internet

INTERNET —

WORLD WIDE WEB —

URLs —

https://www.cgpbooks.co.uk/guestbook

....   Path to a ....
                                              or ....

Domain Name Service (DNS)

A service made of many

1 Browser sends

2 DNS finds

3 Browser requests

4 Web server

Hosting and The Cloud

HOSTING — when a business

THE CLOUD — _____ that offer
a range of services including:

1 Storing

2 Running

3 Providing increased

Pros of the cloud	Cons of the cloud
• Access	• Requires
• Easy to	• Relies on
• No need for	• Stored data can be
• Host provides	• Unclear who has
•	•

Network Security Threats

Four Types of Network Attack

Attack	How it works
1 Data interception and theft	Sensitive _____ travelling on a _____ is intercepted using _____ hardware and software like _____ .
2 Brute-force	_____ software is used to try millions of _____ until one works.
3 Denial of service (DoS)	Hacker prevents users from accessing a network or website by flooding it with _____ .
4 SQL injection	_____ is typed into _____ on a website. If the site doesn't have strong _____ , the hacker can gain access to _____ behind the website. E.g. _____ of customer details.

Malware

MALWARE — software designed to .... or .... a device or network.

Spyware — monitors .... and sends info to the ....

Scareware — tricks user into .... fake problems.

Ransomware — .... files. User pays for ....

.... — gives hackers admin access to the system.

Viruses — attached to ....
Only run or replicate when the file is ....

Worms — like viruses but .... so spread quickly.

Trojans — malware disguised as ....
Do not .... themselves.

Two Types of Social Engineering

SOCIAL ENGINEERING — gaining access to _____ or _____ by using _____ as a system's weak point.

1 Telephone — a person is _____ by someone _____ to be a friend, colleague or company and is persuaded to _____ .

2 Phishing — criminals send _____ pretending to be well-known businesses. They contain links to _____ that ask users to update their _____ , which the criminals steal.

Second Go: ..... / ..... /	**Network Security Threats**

Four Types of Network Attack

Attack	How it works
① Data interception and theft	Sensitive information
② Brute-force	Automated software
③ Denial of service (DoS)	Hacker prevents
④ SQL injection	SQL code is typed into If the site E.g.

Malware

MALWARE — ....
....

Spyware — monitors .... and sends ....

Scareware — tricks ....

Ransomware — .... User ....

Rootkit — gives ....

Viruses — attached ....
         Only run or replicate ....

Worms — like .... so ....

Trojans — malware ....
        Do not ....

Two Types of Social Engineering

SOCIAL ENGINEERING — ....

① Telephone — a person is called

② Phishing — criminals send

    They contain

Network Security Measures

Passwords

Passwords prevent [____] users from accessing a [____].

They should be [____] and changed [____] to protect against [____] attacks.

bossman ✗ ....
B9£l@sTr!y*A ✓ ....

Encryption

Data is translated into a [____] that needs a specific [____] to access.

Secures data sent over a network which limits the effectiveness of [____].

Secures data stored on the network which limits the effectiveness of [____].

User Access Levels

User access levels can control:

- who has access to [____],
- who has [____] access to files,
- who can change [____] of other users.

Limiting the number of people who can access [____] [____] and important files makes social engineering and [____] attacks less effective.

Anti-Malware Software

Anti-malware software prevents malware from [____] a network and the [____] on it.

Antivirus programs [____] and [____] computer viruses.

Firewalls

Firewalls examine all [____] entering and leaving a [____]. They identify [____] using a set of security rules, blocking [____] and unwanted data.

Help to protect against most types of attack including [____], denial of service, [____] and phishing.

Physical Security

Protects physical parts of a network from [____] (e.g. theft and [____]).

- [____] and [____] restrict access to areas like server rooms.
- [____] equipment can deter intruders.

Penetration Testing

Organisations hire specialists to [____] — they identify and report [____] in a network's [____].

The [____] can be fixed to help to protect against [____].

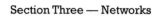

Network Security Measures

Passwords

Passwords prevent

They should be

to protect against

| bossman | ✗ | .... |
| B9£l@sTr!y*A | ✓ | .... |

Encryption

Data is translated into

Secures data sent over a network which

Secures data stored on the network which

User Access Levels

User access levels can control:
- who has

- who has

- who can

Limiting the number of people who can access .... and .... makes .... and .... attacks less effective.

Anti-Malware Software

Anti-malware software

Antivirus programs

Firewalls

Firewalls examine

They identify

Help to protect against most types of attack including

Physical Security

Protects

-

-

Penetration Testing

Organisations hire

The weaknesses can be fixed to help

Mixed Practice Quizzes

Another four topics down. Another four quizzes to come. Crack on with these questions covering pages 45-52 to see what's gone in.

Quiz 1   Date: ...... / ...... / ......

1) What is the world wide web, and which protocol allows access to it? ☑
2) What is 'the cloud'? ☑
3) What is a MAC address? ☑
4) Name four types of network attack. ☑
5) What is a network communication protocol? ☑
6) Give two examples of how encryption can protect against network attacks. ☑
7) What does IP stand for and what does it do? ☑
8) What is anti-malware software? ☑
9) What are five drawbacks of cloud storage? ☑
10) How does Trojan malware infect a computer system? ☑

Total: [   ]

Quiz 2   Date: ...... / ...... / ......

1) What is a brute-force attack? ☑
2) True or false? MAC addresses are given to devices when they connect to a network. ☑
3) Explain how firewalls help to protect against network attacks. ☑
4) How does HTTPS differ from HTTP? ☑
5) Describe how a denial of service attack works. ☑
6) Define the term 'hosting'. ☑
7) What form of attack do strong passwords protect against? ☑
8) What are network layers? ☑
9) What is social engineering? ☑
10) In the following URL, which part is the protocol and which part is the domain name? https://cgpbooks.co.uk/guestbook ☑

Total: [   ]

Mixed Practice Quizzes

Quiz 3   Date: ...... / ...... / ......

1) Define the term 'malware'.
2) What does TCP stand for and what does it do?
3) Give two examples of how physical security is used to protect networks.
4) Give five benefits of cloud storage.
5) How might someone use a phone call as a type of social engineering?
6) In four steps, describe how a domain name service works.
7) Which is the stronger password? "swordfish" or "SwORdF!5h".
8) When is an IP address given to a device?
9) How do user access levels limit the effectiveness of social engineering?
10) Define the terms 'spyware', 'scareware' and 'ransomware'.

Total:

Quiz 4   Date: ...... / ...... / ......

1) What are network standards and why are they important?
2) What is stored on a domain name server?
3) How do viruses infect computer systems? How are worms different?
4) Give three benefits of network layers.
5) What is penetration testing and how does it work?
6) Describe how SQL injection can be used to access private information.
7) Give the name and function of each of these network protocols:
   a) SMTP   b) POP   c) IMAP
8) Outline how phishing works.
9) True or false? The cloud is only used for extra storage.
10) Give three things that user access levels can control.

Total:

Privacy and Ethical Issues

First Go:
..... /..... /.....

Privacy

Personal information can be hard to keep _____ on the _____.

- Websites may ask for a _____ and _____ to set up an account.
- Social media _____ users to share _____, _____, etc.
- Cloud services store _____ on their servers.

Privacy agreements say what a company can do with _____. You have to _____ before using their service.

Privacy _____ can sometimes be changed to make data more _____. They're often fairly relaxed by default.

Users must trust companies to keep their data secure from _____ or _____. Some privacy agreements allow your _____ to be _____ to other companies.

Censorship and Surveillance

CENSORSHIP — controlling what information people can _____.

Three things countries and governments may _____:

1. _____ content or websites supporting _____ activity like _____ or hate speech.
2. _____ content like _____ or pornography.
3. _____ websites or websites that are _____ of the government.

SURVEILLANCE — monitoring what people are _____ on the _____.

- Government intelligence agencies look for _____ or _____ related to _____ activities, e.g. terrorism.
- Internet Service Providers may _____ _____ visited by customers.

Parents and schools also use _____ software to _____ content and _____ activity.

Programs like
....
....
can monitor Internet traffic.

Anonymity

Online anonymity lets people be open and _____ whilst protecting their _____.

Being anonymous online can also cause issues, particularly on _____:

1. CYBERBULLYING — using _____ to deliberately intimidate, insult or humiliate someone _____.
2. _____ — making comments online to deliberately provoke an argument.

 ☑ ☑ ☑

| Second Go: ..... /..... /..... | **Privacy and Ethical Issues** |

Privacy

Personal information can be _____ .

- Websites may ask for
- Social media encourages users
- Cloud services

Privacy agreements say what a

You have to

Privacy settings can sometimes be

Users must trust companies to keep

Censorship and Surveillance

CENSORSHIP — _____ .
Three things countries and governments may _____ :

1
2
3

SURVEILLANCE —

- Government intelligence agencies look for

- Internet Service Providers may keep

Programs like
....
....
can monitor
Internet traffic.

Parents and schools also use

Anonymity

Online anonymity lets people be open and _____ whilst protecting their _____ .
Being anonymous online can also cause issues, particularly on _____ :

1 CYBERBULLYING — using

2 TROLLING — making

 ☑ 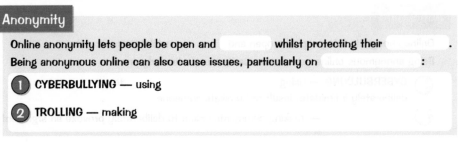 ☑ ☑

Cultural Issues and Wellbeing

Three Causes of the Digital Divide

DIGITAL DIVIDE — the _____ caused by unequal _____ to technology.

1 Devices and an _____ connection can be too _____ .

2 _____ areas often have greater network coverage than _____ areas.

3 People may have difficulty adopting new technology — usually due to not being _____ or not _____ .

There is a global divide due to different _____ to technology in different _____ . Projects and charities have been set up to _____ the digital and global divide.

Five Examples of Cultural Changes

1 Selfies — _____ and smartphone cameras make sharing _____ easy. This may make people more _____ .

2 Viral videos — the Internet allows videos to rapidly _____ . People and organisations try to use this for _____ .

3 _____ — allows people to publish writing, art and other media. Gives a _____ to those ignored by mainstream media.

4 _____ allow people to listen to music and watch television, often through a _____ .

5 The sharing economy is driven by services in which people use new _____ to make money from things they _____ .
  • Spare rooms rented to tourists.
  • Cars used for _____ or _____ services.

Wellbeing and Health

Impacts on Social Wellbeing

• _____ make it easy for work to intrude into other areas of life. This can be _____ for employees.

• Face-to-face interactions can be _____ as social life and working life moves _____ .

• Companies regularly release new _____ which people can feel _____ into buying.

Three tech-related health problems:

1 _____ from looking at a screen for too long or too closely.

2 _____ caused by using devices for extended periods of time.

3 Back pain resulting from poor _____ or bad _____ .

Section Four — Issues

Second Go:
...../...../.....

Cultural Issues and Wellbeing

Three Causes of the Digital Divide

DIGITAL DIVIDE —

1

2

3 People may have difficulty adopting new technology — usually due to

There is a global divide due to

Five Examples of Cultural Changes

1 Selfies —

This may make

2 Viral videos —

People and organisations

3 Social media —

Gives a voice

4 Streaming services

5 The sharing economy is driven by

• .... rented to tourists.
• ....
....·

Wellbeing and Health

Impacts on Social Wellbeing
• Smartphones

• Face-to-face interactions

• Companies regularly release

Three tech-related health problems:

Environmental Issues

Natural Resources

Electronic devices contain lots of [_____].

- Crude oil is used to [_____] [_____] for packaging, casing and other parts.

- Precious metals are used in [_____] and [_____]. E.g. _____, _____, copper, mercury, palladium, platinum and indium.

Non-renewable resources like [____], [____] and [_____] are used to generate electricity.

Extracting these materials uses lots of [_____], creates [_____] (e.g. greenhouse gases) and depletes scarce [_____].

Electricity Usage

Devices use a lot of [_____] in the form of electricity.

Computers and servers also generate [_____]. They are often cooled using [_____] or [_____] rooms which uses even more [_____].

There are ways to reduce electricity waste:

Problem	Solution
Desktops, laptops and smartphones are left [_____].	[_____] and [_____] modes reduce power consumption.
Servers don't use all of their [_____].	Multiple [_____] servers can run on one [_____] server.

E-Waste

Millions of [_____] are [_____] every year.

Three ways device manufacturers and [_____] can contribute to this problem:

1. Providing short [_____].
2. Pricing — [_____] to replace than [_____].
3. Marketing to convince people to [_____].

To cut costs, lots of [_____] is sent to [_____] where regulations are less strict. Most ends up in [_____] and can be a hazard — can leak into groundwater and harm wildlife.

The Waste [_____] and [_____] Equipment (WEEE) directive covers:

- Disposing of [_____] safely.
- Promoting [_____], e.g. refurbishing broken devices.
- [_____] materials, e.g. extracting precious metals.

Section Four — Issues

| Second Go: ..... / ..... / ..... | **Environmental Issues** |

Natural Resources

Electronic devices _____.

- Crude oil

- Precious metals

  E.g. ...., ..., ..., mercury, palladium, platinum and indium.

Non-renewable resources

Extracting these materials uses

Electricity Usage

Devices use

Computers and servers

There are ways to reduce electricity waste:

Problem	Solution
Desktops, laptops and smartphones	
Servers	

E-Waste

Millions of _____.

Three ways _____
can contribute to this problem:

1 Providing   **2** Pricing —   **3** Marketing

To cut costs, lots of e-waste is sent to

The _____ (WEEE) directive covers:
- Disposing
- Promoting
-

Legislation and Licensing

First Go:
..... /..... /.....

Six Principles of the Data Protection Act 2018

1. Data must be used in a _____, _____ and transparent way.

2. Data must be used for _____ _____.

3. Data gathered should be _____ and not excessive.

4. Data must be _____ and kept up to _____.

5. Data should not be kept _____ than necessary.

6. Data should be kept _____ and _____.

Data subjects have the right to see, amend and delete their _____ _____.

Organisations must register with the _____ before collecting personal data.

Copyright, Designs and Patents Act 1988

Copyright covers _____ or _____ content, e.g. videos, music, software.

Patents cover _____ — they protect ideas and _____.

All intellectual property is _____ protected, so it's illegal to _____, _____ and _____ material without the correct permission.

Copyright and patent holders can grant _____ to use material for a _____.

Three Offences under the Computer Misuse Act 1990

Introduced to stop _____ and _____ crime.

1. Gaining unauthorised access to a _____ or _____.

2. Gaining unauthorised access in order to _____.

3. Unauthorised _____ of computer material.

Software Licensing

SOFTWARE LICENCE — a legal .... stating how software can be ....:

OPEN SOURCE SOFTWARE — source code made _____ .

Pros	Cons
• Usually _____	• Irregular _____
• Can be legally _____	_____ if unpopular
• Often _____	• Limited _____
• Reliable and _____ if popular	• No _____ or support

PROPRIETARY SOFTWARE — only _____ is available.

Pros	Cons
• _____ and support	• Often _____
• Well-tested and _____	• Can't legally be _____
• Usually regularly _____	• Old versions may not be _____

Second Go: ..... / ..... /	**Legislation and Licensing**

Six Principles of the Data Protection Act 2018

① Data must be used in a

② Data must be used for

③ Data gathered should be

④ Data must be

⑤ Data should not be kept

⑥ Data should be kept

Data subjects have the right to see, amend and delete their ....

Organisations must register with the _____ before collecting personal data.

Copyright, Designs and Patents Act 1988

Copyright covers

Patents cover

All intellectual property is

Copyright and patent holders can

Three Offences under the Computer Misuse Act 1990

Introduced to stop _____ .

① Gaining

② Gaining

③ Unauthorised

Software Licensing

SOFTWARE LICENCE — ....
....

OPEN SOURCE SOFTWARE —	
Pros	**Cons**
• • • •	• • •

PROPRIETARY SOFTWARE —	
Pros	**Cons**
• • •	• • •

Mixed Practice Quizzes

Well that was a quick section, but there were a few hefty topics in there.
Have a go at answering these questions covering p.55-62 to see what's stuck.

Quiz 1   Date: ...... / ...... / ......

1) Give three non-renewable resources that are used
   to generate electricity. Why is this a problem?
2) What is trolling?
3) List five examples of cultural changes driven by technology.
4) What is it illegal to do under the Copyright, Designs and Patents Act 1988?
5) Why is it hard to keep personal information private on the Internet?
6) According to the Data Protection Act 2018, what must
   organisations do before they can begin collecting data?
7) What is meant by the 'digital divide'?
8) Give three offences under the Computer Misuse Act 1990.
9) List three things countries and governments may restrict access to online.
10) What is e-waste?

Total:

Quiz 2   Date: ...... / ...... / ......

1) Servers can generate excess heat and need to be cooled,
   what environmental issue does this cause?
2) Give two examples of surveillance on the Internet.
3) What are three things the WEEE directive covers?
4) Give one way that someone on the Internet
   can make their data more private.
5) List the six principles of the Data Protection Act 2018.
6) Give three causes of the digital divide.
7) What is the difference between copyright and patents?
8) What is a cultural issue with the ease of taking and sharing photos online?
9) Why might someone want to use open source
   software over proprietary software?
10) Suggest one way to reduce electricity waste in everyday devices.

Total:

Mixed Practice Quizzes

Quiz 3   Date: ...... / ...... / ......

1) What is cyberbullying? ☑
2) What is open source software? How is proprietary software different? ☑
3) Name two raw materials used to make electronic devices. ☑
4) What are privacy agreements? ☑
5) What is a software licence? ☑
6) What software can be used to filter content online, and who might use it? ☑
7) Give an example of how e-waste can be an environmental hazard. ☑
8) What are three tech-related health problems? ☑
9) What are the disadvantages of using open source software? ☑
10) What is the 'global divide'? ☑

Total:

Quiz 4   Date: ...... / ...... / ......

1) Define the term 'censorship'. ☑
2) How might servers be wasting electricity? Suggest a potential solution. ☑
3) Give two examples of services used as part of the sharing economy. ☑
4) What are the advantages of using proprietary software? ☑
5) Give a benefit of online anonymity. ☑
6) According to the Data Protection Act 2018, what rights do data subjects have regarding their personal data? ☑
7) List three impacts that technological changes may have on social wellbeing. ☑
8) Give three ways device manufacturers and retailers may be contributing to the e-waste problem. ☑
9) Why was the Computer Misuse Act 1990 introduced? ☑
10) What environmental issues does using precious metals in wiring and circuit boards cause? ☑

Total:

Computational Thinking & Pseudocode

First Go:
..... /..... /.....

Three Key Techniques for Computational Thinking

① DECOMPOSITION — _____ a complex problem into lots of _____ ones.

② ABSTRACTION — _____ a problem by picking out the _____ bits of information.

③ ALGORITHMIC THINKING — coming up with a series of _____ to get from a _____ to a _____ .

EXAMPLE

Find the quickest route by car between two places.

① <u>Decomposition</u>: What is the _____ of each route?
                    What are the _____ limits on each route?

② <u>Abstraction</u>:

Details to _____	Details to _____
Distance as the crow flies	_____ route along the roads
Road names	Traffic information

③ <u>Algorithmic thinking</u>:

1) List all _____ routes.   3) Calculate _____ for each route.
2) Find _____ of each route.   4) Find route with _____ time.

Pseudocode

ALGORITHM — a _____ _____ for solving a problem.

PSEUDOCODE — a simple way of writing an _____ without using a specific _____ .

There are no exact rules, but good pseudocode will be:

• readable and easy to _____

• not too vague

• _____ like a piece of code

• easy to _____ into any language

EXAMPLE

Design an algorithm to filter items on a website so only those that cost £10 or less are shown.

```
n = number of items        Loop goes
                           through each
                           item one by one.
for i = ...... to ......
  itemPrice = ............ of item i
  if ................ <= ............ then
     ............ item i
  else                    Checks whether
     ............ item i   the item should
  endif                   be shown.
next i
```

Second Go:
...../...../.....

Computational Thinking & Pseudocode

Three Key Techniques for Computational Thinking

1 **DECOMPOSITION —**

2 **ABSTRACTION —**

3 **ALGORITHMIC THINKING —**

EXAMPLE Find the quickest route by car between two places.

1 <u>Decomposition</u>: What is the ....?
                      What are the ....?

2 <u>Abstraction</u>:

Details to	Details to ....
Distance as the crow flies	.... route along the roads
....	....

3 <u>Algorithmic thinking</u>:

1) .... all .... routes.   3) .... for each route.
2) .... of each route.   4) .... route with .... time.

Pseudocode

ALGORITHM —

PSEUDOCODE —

There are no exact rules,
but good pseudocode will be:

• readable and easy to ....
• not ....
• .... like a piece of code
• easy to .... into any language

EXAMPLE

Design an algorithm to filter items on a website so only those that cost £10 or less are shown.

```
n = number of items
```

 ☑ ☑ ☑

Flowcharts

Flowchart Symbols

Symbol	When It's Used
Start / Stop	At the .... and .... of the algorithm
Inputs / Outputs	For values that are .... or ....
Processes	E.g. for instructions and ....

Symbol	When It's Used
Decision	For a .... — often a 'yes or no'
Sub Program	To reference other ....
→	To connect boxes and show ....

Sequence

SEQUENCE — only has ⬜ ⬜ from start to stop.

A flowchart to find the cost of a hotel stay at £40 per night.

Start → Input number of .... → cost = ... × £....... → Output .... → Stop

Selection

SELECTION — has ⬜ which give multiple ⬜ from start to stop.

A flowchart to check a user is older than 12 before allowing access.

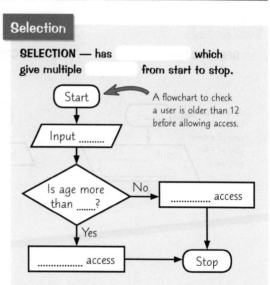

Start → Input .... → Is age more than ....? — No → .... access → Stop; Yes → .... access → Stop

Iteration

ITERATION — contains a ⬜ that lets you ⬜ a task.

A flowchart for a binary search. You could write a sub program to do this.

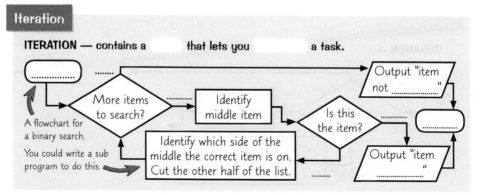

More items to search? / Identify middle item / Is this the item? / Identify which side of the middle the correct item is on. Cut the other half of the list. / Output "item not ...." / Output "item ...."

Flowcharts

Flowchart Symbols

Symbol	When It's Used	Symbol	When It's Used
	At the .... and .... of the algorithm		For a .... — often a ....
	For .... that are .... or		To .... other ....
	E.g. for .... and		To .... boxes and show ....

Sequence

SEQUENCE —

A flowchart to find the cost of a hotel stay at £40 per night.

Start

Input ....
....

Selection

SELECTION —

A flowchart to check a user is older than 12 before allowing access.

Start

Input ....

Iteration

ITERATION —

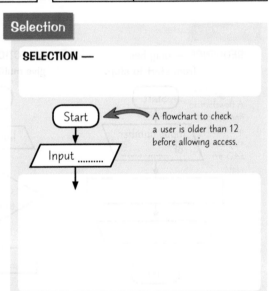

A flowchart for a binary search.

You could write a sub program to do this.

.... items to search?

.... middle item

Identify which .... of the middle the correct item is on. Cut the other half of the list.

 ☑ ☑ ☑

Search Algorithms

Binary Search

The list must be ....

EXAMPLE

Use a binary search to find the number 32 in this list:

| 4 | 7 | 13 | 18 | 28 | 32 | 35 |

1. Find the .... item — for n items, do $\frac{(n + 1)}{2}$ and .... if needed.

2. If this is the item you ...., then .... the search.

3. If not, ... the two items. If the item you want comes .... the .... item, cut the .... half of the list. Otherwise cut the .... half.

4. Repeat steps ① - ③ on the .... of the list you're left with until you .... the item you want or .... of items.

There are 7 items, middle item is (....... + 1) ÷ 2 = ... item is .... and .... < .... so cut .... half of the list.

There are 3 items left, middle item is (....... + 1) ÷ 2 = ... item is .... so item .... , the search is ....

Linear Search

EXAMPLE

Use a linear search to find the number 32 in this list:

| 4 | 7 | 13 | 18 | 28 | 32 | 35 |

1. Look at the .... item in the list.

2. If this is the item you ...., then .... the search.

3. If not, look at the .... item along in the list.

4. Repeat steps .... - .... until you .... the item you want or you reach the .... of the list.

Check .... item: .... ≠ 32
Look at next item: .... ≠ 32
Look at next item: .... ≠ 32
Look at next item: .... ≠ 32
Look at next item: .... ≠ 32
Look at next item: ....
Item .... — search complete.

Comparing Search Algorithms

	PROS	CONS
Binary Search	• Efficient at searching .... lists	• List must be .... first
Linear Search	• Simple • Works on .... lists	• Inefficient at searching .... lists

Section Five — Algorithms

Second Go: ..... /..... /.....

Search Algorithms

Binary Search

The list must be _____

1. **Find**

2. **If this is**

3. **If not,**

   If the item you want comes

   Otherwise

4. **Repeat steps**

EXAMPLE

Use a binary search to find the number 32 in this list:

4	7	13	18	28	32	35

There are _____, middle item is

_____ = _____.

_____ item is _____ and _____

so cut _____ of the list.

_____

There are _____ left, middle item is

_____ = _____.

_____ item is _____ so

_____ , the search is _____ .

Linear Search

1. **Look at**

2. **If this is**

3. **If not,**

4. **Repeat steps**

EXAMPLE

Use a linear search to find the number 32 in this list:

4	7	13	18	28	32	35

Check _____ :

Look at next item:

Look at next item:

Look at next item:

Look at next item:

Look at next item:

Comparing Search Algorithms

	PROS	CONS
Binary Search		
Linear Search		

Section Five — Algorithms

Bubble Sort and Insertion Sort

Bubble Sort

1. Look at the .... items in the list.

2. If they're in the right order, ... them. Otherwise, ... them.

3. Move on to the .... of items (2nd and 3rd entries) and repeat step .....

4. Repeat step ..... until you reach the .... — this is one pass.
The .... item is now in the correct place, so don't include it in the next pass.

5. Repeat steps ..... - ..... until there are .... in a pass.

EXAMPLE

Use a bubble sort to write these letters in alphabetical order:

C A K E

The algorithm is only complete when there are .... in a pass.

1st pass:

C A K E   Compare C and A – .... them.

___ K E   Compare ...... and K – .... them.

___ E   Compare ...... and E – .... them.

End of first pass.

2nd pass:

Compare ...... and ...... – ...... them.

Compare ...... and ...... – ...... them.

so the list is sorted.

Insertion Sort

1. Look at the .... in the list.

2. Compare it to all items .... it and .... the item into the right place.

3. Repeat step ..... for each .... item until the .... item in the list has been .... in the correct place.

EXAMPLE

Use an insertion sort to order these numbers from smallest to largest:

6 2 7 3 1 4

6 2 7 3 1 4   Insert ...... before ....

___ 7 3 1 4   No insertion.

___ 3 1 4   Insert ...... between 2 and 6.

___ 1 4   Insert ...... before ....

___ 4   Insert ...... between 3 and 6.

___   Last item inserted, so the list is sorted.

Section Five — Algorithms

Bubble Sort and Insertion Sort

Bubble Sort

1. Look at the
2. If they're in the
3. Move on to the next
4. Repeat step
5. Repeat steps

EXAMPLE

Use a bubble sort to write these letters in alphabetical order:

C A K E

The algorithm is only complete when there are ....

1st pass:

| |
| |
| |
| |

Compare
Compare
Compare

2nd pass:

| |
| |

Compare
Compare

Insertion Sort

1. Look at the

2. Compare it to

3. Repeat step 2 for

EXAMPLE

Use an insertion sort to order these numbers from smallest to largest:

| 6 | 2 | 7 | 3 | 1 | 4 |

6 2 7 3 1 4

Merge Sort

Merge Sort

1 Split the list into two sub-lists — start the .... sub-list at the .... item.

2 Repeat step **1** on each sub-list until all sub-lists only contain ....

3 Merge pairs of sub-lists back together. Each time you merge two sub-lists, ... the items into the ....

4 Repeat step .... until you've merged all the sub-lists together.

Merge sorts are efficient for computers because:

• .... lists are easier to sort.
• It's quick to merge .... lists.

EXAMPLE

Use a merge sort to order these numbers from largest to smallest.

4	9	1	5	3	6	8	7

| 4 | 9 | 1 | 5 | |

| 4 | 9 | | 1 | 5 | | | | | |

| 4 | 9 | 1 | 5 | | | | |

| 9 | 4 | 5 | 1 | | | | |

| 9 | 5 | 4 | 1 | | | | |

| | | | | | | | |

Comparing Sorting Algorithms

	PROS	CONS
Bubble Sort and Insertion Sort	• Simple and .... to implement • Quick to check if a list is .... • Doesn't need much ....,' sorting only uses original list	• Inefficient on .... lists
Merge Sort	• Efficient on .... lists • Running .... unaffected by .... of items in original list	• Slower on .... lists • Goes through whole process even if list is .... • Uses more .... in order to create sub-lists

74

Second Go: ..... /..... /.....	# Merge Sort

Merge Sort

① Split the list into

② Repeat step 1 on

③ Merge pairs of

④ Repeat step

Merge sorts are efficient for computers because:

* [_____] lists are easier to sort.
* It's quick to merge [_____] lists.

EXAMPLE

Use a merge sort to order these numbers from largest to smallest.

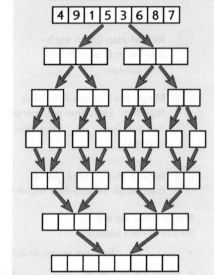

4 9 1 5 3 6 8 7

Comparing Sorting Algorithms

	PROS	CONS
Bubble Sort and Insertion Sort	• Simple and • Quick to • Doesn't need much	• Inefficient on
Merge Sort	• Efficient on • Running	• Slower on • Goes through • Uses more

 ☑ ☑ ☑

Mixed Practice Quizzes

Have a go at the next lot of quizzes to see how much has gone in from pages 65-74. And no, you can't write an algorithm to do it for you.

Quiz 1   Date: ...... / ...... / ......

1) Which of the following flowchart symbols would you use for a question/decision? ⬭ ◇ ▭ ▱

2) Name three techniques for computational thinking.

3) What counts as one pass in a bubble sort?

4) What is an algorithm?

5) Describe how to carry out a merge sort in four steps.

6) What is decomposition?

7)* Why would a binary search not be suitable for the following list?
54, 21, 17, 5, 20, 13

8) How do sequence and selection flowcharts differ?

9)* Draw a flowchart to represent how fingerprint recognition on a smartphone works.

10) What are the advantages of using an insertion sort?

Total:

Quiz 2   Date: ...... / ...... / ......

1) Describe how to carry out an insertion sort in three steps.

2) True or false? Merge sorts are unaffected by the order of the original list.

3) Give four properties that all good pseudocode should have.

4) What is one disadvantage of the bubble sort algorithm?

5)* To design her new app, Mary breaks it down into features and considers each one separately. Which aspect of computational thinking is this?

6) Which sorting algorithm would be best to use on a list of 200 000 items?

7) When are ▱ symbols used in a flowchart?

8)* Use a merge sort to write the letters of "COMPUTER" in alphabetical order.

9)* In a linear search the best case scenario is if the item you're looking for is the first item in the list. What is the worst case scenario?

10) What is the purpose of arrows in a flowchart?

Total:

Mixed Practice Quizzes

Quiz 3 | Date: ...... / ...... / ......

1) What is pseudocode?
2) When are ⬜ symbols used in a flowchart?
3) Describe how to carry out a bubble sort in five steps.
4) Give two advantages of using a linear search over a binary search.
5) How does using abstraction help to solve problems?
6) What must an iteration flowchart contain?
7)* When calculating the cost of a journey, you might first find some route options, then calculate the cost of each, and then choose the cheapest. Which aspect of computational thinking is this?
8)* Use a bubble sort to order these numbers from largest to smallest: 24, 52, 36, 4, 28
9)* Use a binary search to find "Rudolph" in the following list: Bob, Comet, Cupid, Rudolph, Vixen.
10) Give three disadvantages of using a merge sort.

Total:

Quiz 4 | Date: ...... / ...... / ......

1) Define the term 'algorithmic thinking'.
2) Describe how to carry out a binary search in four steps.
3) Draw a start/stop flowchart symbol.
4) Why might you choose to use a binary search over a linear search?
5) What criteria is used to determine the end of a bubble sort?
6)* Use an insertion sort to write the letters of "COLIN" in alphabetical order.
7)* True or false? A bubble sort will take the same time on two different lists if they have the same length.
8)* When planning a bus journey, you might focus on buses that arrive on time and ignore the ones that would make you late. Which aspect of computational thinking is this?
9)* Use a linear search to find 28 in the following list: 98, 42, 28, 50, 1
10) Give two reasons why merge sorts are efficient for computers.

Total:

Section Five — Algorithms

Data Types & Random Numbers

Five Basic Data Types

1 _____
- Whole numbers
- E.g. 0, –35, 1254

2 REAL/FLOAT
- _____
- E.g. 3.14, –150.2

3 _____
- Two values
- E.g. True/False, 1/0, yes/no

4 CHARACTER
- One _____ , _____ or
- E.g. "X", "5", "?", "#"

5 _____
- Text — a collection of _____
- E.g. "Xm2Pe5", "@cgpbooks.co.uk"

Casting

Functions can _____ between data types...

`int("5")` ← _____ "5" to _____ 5

_____ or `float(3)` ← Integer 3 to decimal 3.0

_____ ← Integer 123 to string "123"

`bool(0)` ← Integer 0 to Boolean _____

... and between characters and **ASCII** numbers.

_____ ← Character 'A' to integer 65

`CHR(65)` ← Integer ____ to character '__'

Choosing Data Types

Using correct data types makes code more:

1 Memory _____

2 Robust

3 _____

Using the wrong data type could mean your code gives _____ or _____ results.

Random Number Generation

Generate random numbers by using this function. → _____ (x, y)

x and y can be _____ or _____.

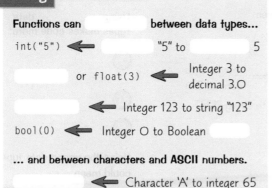

_____ ← A random integer between 10 and 99 (including 10 and 99).

_____ ← A random real number between 3.0 and 7.0 (including 3.0 and 7.0).

Random numbers can be used to make _____ things happen in your program. E.g. to make choices and set attributes randomly.

Data Types & Random Numbers

Five Basic Data Types

1 _____
- _____
- E.g. 0, –35, 1254

2 _____
- _____
- E.g. 3.14, –150.2

3 _____
- _____
- E.g. _____ / _____, 1/0, yes/no

4 _____
- _____
- E.g. "X", "5", "?", "#"

5 _____
- _____
- E.g. "Xm2Pe5", "@cgpbooks.co.uk"

Casting

Functions can _____ between _____ ...

`int("5")` ⟵ _____ to _____

_____ or _____ ⟵ Integer 3 to decimal 3.0

_____ ⟵ Integer 123 to string "123"

`bool(0)` ⟵ Integer 0 to _____

... and between _____ and _____ .

_____ ⟵ Character 'A' to integer 65

`CHR(65)` ⟵ _____

Choosing Data Types

Using _____ data types makes code more:

1 _____

2 _____

3 _____

Using the wrong data type could mean

Random Number Generation

Generate random numbers by using this function. ⟶ _____

x and y can be _____ or _____ .

_____ ⟵ A random integer between 10 and 99 (including _____).

_____ ⟵ A random real number between 3.0 and 7.0 (including _____).

Random numbers can be used to _____ _____ . E.g. to make _____ and set _____ randomly.

Operators

Arithmetic Operators

Perform maths functions on two .... or .... values.

Operator	Function	Example	Result
	Addition	4 ⬜ 5	9
-		6 - 9	-3
	Multiplication	3 ⬜ 8	24
/		35 / 5	7
	Exponentiation	2 ⬜ 3	8
DIV		19 DIV 4	4
MOD		19 MOD 4	3

.... is used to evaluate expressions, so $9 - 6/3$ gives $9 - 2 = 7$.

DIV gives the .... part of a division.

MOD gives the .... of a division.

Comparison Operators

Compare two .... and return a .... value (........... or ....).

Operator	Meaning	Returns True	Returns False
	is equal to	"A" ⬜ "A"	"A" ⬜ "B"
!=	is ⬜ to	6.5 != 7.0	7 != 7
<	is ⬜ than	8 < 9	6.5 < 6.5
>	is ⬜ than	10 > 9	12 > 13
	is less than or equal to	6 ⬜ 6	6 ⬜ 5
	is greater than or equal to	1 ⬜ 0	2 - 3 ⬜ 0

Comparison operators are checked after other operators are performed.

Boolean Operators

Work with .... values/expressions and return .... or ....

Operator	How it Works	Returns True	Returns False
NOT	Returns True when the expression is ⬜.	NOT(6 < 5)	NOT(4 <= 5)
AND	Returns True when both expressions are ⬜.	1 <= 1 AND 2 == 2	7 > 5 AND 0 < 1
OR	Returns True when either expression is ⬜.	2 > 5 OR 3 < 6	4 >= 8 OR 6 == 9

Order of operations: brackets, ..., ... then ....

Second Go: ..... / ..... / .....

Operators

Arithmetic Operators

Perform .... on ....

Operator	Function	Example	Result
	Addition	4 ☐ 5	
–		6 - 9	
	Multiplication	3 ☐ 8	
/		35 / 5	
	Exponentiation	2 ☐ 3	
		19 ☐ 4	4
		19 ☐ 4	3

.... is used to .... expressions, so 9 – 6/3 gives .... = ...

.... gives the .... part of a division.

.... gives the .... of a division.

Comparison Operators

Compare two .... and return a .... (............ or ....).

Operator	Meaning	Returns ☐	Returns ☐
	is equal to	"A" ☐ "A"	"A" ☐ "B"
!=		6.5 != 7.0	7 != 7
<		8 < 9	6.5 < 6.5
>		10 > 9	12 > 13
	is .... than or .... to	6 ☐ 6	6 ☐ 5
	is .... than or .... to	1 ☐ 0	2 - 3 ☐ 0

Comparison operators are checked after other operators are performed.

Boolean Operators

Work with .... and return ....

Operator	How it Works	Returns ☐	Returns ☐
NOT	Returns True when	NOT(6 < 5)	NOT(4 <= 5)
AND	Returns True when	1 <= 1 AND 2 == 2	7 > 5 AND 0 < 1
OR	Returns True when	2 > 5 OR 3 < 6	4 >= 8 OR 6 == 9

Order of operations: ....

Section Six — Programming

Boolean Logic

Three Types of Logic Gates

Logic gates are special [_____] built into computer chips. They receive [_____] data, apply a [_____] operation, then output a [_____] result.

| Name | Symbol | Truth Table |

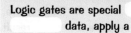

1 [_____] Input —▷o— Output

Input	Output
0	
1	

2 [_____] Input A / Input B —— Output

Input A	Input B	Output
0	0	0
0	1	
1	0	0
1	1	

3 [_____] Input A / Input B —— Output

Input A	Input B	Output
0	0	
0	1	1
1	0	
1	1	1

Combining Logic Gates

Logic gates can be combined into circuits.
For example, [_____] followed by [_____]:

A —— B ——▷o— P

Written as P = [_____]

Operations in brackets are done first.

A	B	A [____] B	(A [____] B)
0	0	0	1
0	1		
1	0	0	1
1	1		

Two-Level Logic Circuits

Two-level means each [_____] passes through [_____] gates.

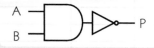

A —▷o—
B ——
C —— } — Q

Short Boolean algebra notation.

A	B	C	¬A	B∧C	Q = ¬A∨(B∧C)
0	0	0			
1	1	0			
1	1	1			

Written as Q = [_____]

  ☑   ☑   ☑

Second Go:
..... /..... /.....

Boolean Logic

Three Types of Logic Gates

Logic gates are special [blank] built into [blank]. They receive [blank] data, apply a [blank], then output a [blank] result.

Name	Symbol	Truth Table

1 [blank] Input | [blank] | Output

Input	Output

2 [blank] Input A / Input B | [blank] | Output

Input A	Input B	Output

3 [blank] Input A / Input B | [blank] | Output

Input A	Input B	Output

Combining Logic Gates

Logic gates can be combined into circuits.
For example, AND followed by NOT:

A —
       — P
B —

Written as P = [blank]

Operations in brackets are done first.

A	B	A	B	(A	B)

Two-Level Logic Circuits

Two-level means [blank]

Short Boolean algebra notation.

A —
B —   — Q
C —

Written as Q = (NOT A) OR (B AND C)

A	B	C	¬A	B∧C	Q = ¬A∨(B∧C)
0	0	0			
1	1	0			
1	1	1			

Variables and Strings

Storing Data Values

1 Constants can't [_____] while the code is running.

```
const daysInWeek = 7
```

2 Variables can [_____].

```
length = 3
length = length * 10
```

The [_____] operator (=) assigns values.

- Variable [_____] (identifier) on the left.
- [_____] or [_____] on the right.
- Stored [_____] can be accessed later in a program.

Inputs and Outputs

Use input() to [____] data [____] a user.

```
name = input("Enter name:")
```
Put a string here to display it to the user.

Use print() to [_____] data [____] a user.

```
print("An error occurred.")
```

Manipulating Strings

Strings are usually written in [_____].
Use the + operator to [_____] (join) strings.

Strings are indexed from [____] :

M	a	g	i	c

Function	Returns	Example (s = "Magic")	Result
upper		s.upper	MAGIC
lower			magic
	No. of characters		5
left(n)		s.left(3)	Mag
	Last n characters		ic
substring(a, b)	String starting at .... a, ... b	s.substring(....,....)	agi

EXAMPLE

Reformat the variable 'name' so that only the first character is capitalised.

```
first = name.[_____]          ← Extract the first letter.
rest = name.[_____] (name.[____] - 1)   ← Extract everything after.
name = [_____] + [_____]          ← Change case and join.
```

Section Six — Programming

Variables and Strings

Storing Data Values

1 Constants can't _____ while

```
const daysInWeek = 7
```

2 Variables can _____ .

```
length = 3
length = length * 10
```

The _____ operator (=)
_____ .

- _____
  (_____) on the left.

- _____ or _____
  on the right.

- Stored _____ can be
  _____ later in a program.

Inputs and Outputs

Use input() to _____ .

Use print() to _____ .

```
name = ...........("Enter name:")
...........("An error occurred.")
```

Manipulating Strings

Strings are usually written in _____ .

Use the + operator to _____ .

Strings are _____ from _____ :

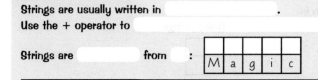

Function	Returns	Example (s = "Magic")	Result
			MAGIC
			magic
			5
			Mag
			ic
			agi

EXAMPLE

Reformat the variable 'name' so that only the first character is capitalised.

```
first =
rest =
name =
```

Mixed Practice Quizzes

Which operator are you? Take a quiz to find out... Just kidding — you're clearly a '>', as in, greater than these quizzes that cover the topics on pages 77-84.

Quiz 1   Date: ...... / ...... / ......

1)* What data type can store the value –123 but not 1.23?
2) What is the arithmetic operator for division?
3) Draw the logic symbol for a **NOT** gate.
4)* Does the expression '8 < 3 OR 5 > 1' return True or False?
5) Describe the type of data that can be stored as a string.
6) Explain the difference between a constant and a variable.
7) What function can be used to get data from a user?
8)* x = "Apple pie". What is the value of x.length?
9) Give three ways in which using correct data types can improve code.
10) Complete a truth table for an **AND** gate.

Total:

Quiz 2   Date: ...... / ...... / ......

1) Which data type can take only two values?
2) What is the operator = used for?
3) Give one reason for using random number generation in a program.
4) Complete a truth table for an **OR** gate.
5) What function is represented by the * operator?
6) What does the term 'casting' mean?
7)* Write a comparison to check if the variable x is less than or equal to 9.
8)* If a = "3" and b = "5", what is the value of a + b?
9) Draw the logic symbol for an **AND** gate.
10)* What is the index of the character 'x' in the string "index"?

Total:

Mixed Practice Quizzes

Quiz 3 Date: ...... / ...... / ......

1)* What is the result of $3 \wedge 2$?
2) Draw the logic symbol for an OR gate.
3) Name a data type that can be used for numbers with a decimal part.
4) What function is used to display data to a user?
5) Describe the possible outputs of random(1.0, 2.0).
6)* What value does bool(1) return?
7) Complete a truth table for a NOT gate.
8)* Describe the values of x for which 'NOT (x < 3)' is True.
9)* x = "Hello". What does x.substring(1, 2) return?
10) Explain what the function s.right(n) does for a string s and integer n.

Total:

Quiz 4 Date: ...... / ...... / ......

1)* Does '6.2 != 2.6' return True or False?
2) What data type can only store a single digit, letter or symbol?
3)* True or false? If s = "amal", then s.upper returns "Amal".
4) Explain the purpose of the functions CHR() and ASC().
5) Define the term 'string concatenation'.
6) What does the operator < mean?
7)* Draw a logic diagram for the expression NOT (A OR B).
8)* s = "string". What does s.left(3) return?
9)* What is the value of 17 MOD 5?
10)* Complete a truth table for the expression (NOT A) AND (NOT B).

Total:

Selection

IF Statements

Check if a condition is _____ or _____ before running code.

IF statements start with ' ____ [condition] ____ ' and end with ' _____ '. The ' ____ ' part is optional.

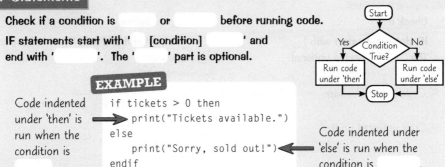

Start

Condition True?

Yes — Run code under 'then'

No — Run code under 'else'

Stop

EXAMPLE

Code indented under 'then' is run when the condition is _____.

```
if tickets > 0 then
    print("Tickets available.")
else
    print("Sorry, sold out!")
endif
```

Code indented under 'else' is run when the condition is _____.

IF-ELSEIF Statements

Check different _____ and run the code under the first one that is _____.

EXAMPLE

```
if score > 90 then
    print("Amazing – well done!")
elseif score > 60 then
    print("Great effort!")
elseif score > 30 then
    print("Room for improvement!")
else
    print("Keep practising!")
endif
```

What to do if ...

...first condition is _____.

...first condition is _____, second condition is _____.

...first and second conditions are _____, third condition is _____.

...all conditions are _____.

SWITCH Statements

Check if a variable has specific _____ before running code.

EXAMPLE

The _____ of 'answer' determines which _____ to use.

Each case should be _____ to the same place.

```
answer = input("What is 5 - 7?")
switch answer:
    case -2:
        print("Correct!")
    case 2:
        print("Forgot minus sign?")
    default:
        print("Wrong!")
endswitch
```

Don't forget colons.

SWITCH only checks a single ...., not multiple .... like IF-ELSEIF.

Default case comes at the end and used if no other _____ is correct.

Selection

IF Statements

Check if _____ before _____ .

IF statements start with '_____' and end with '_____'.

The '_____' part is optional.

EXAMPLE

Code indented under '_____' is run when _____ .

..... tickets > 0 ....
→ print("Tickets available.")

Code indented under '_____' is run when _____ .

....
→ print("Sorry, sold out!")
....

IF-ELSEIF Statements

Check _____ and run the

code under _____ .

EXAMPLE

..... score > 90 ....
print("Amazing — well done!")
.... score > 60 ....
print("Great effort!")
.... score > 30 ....
print("Room for improvement!")
....
print("Keep practising!")
....

What to do if ...

... _____ condition is _____ .

... _____ condition is _____ ,

_____ condition is _____ .

... _____ and _____ conditions are _____ , condition is _____ .

... _____ conditions are _____ .

SWITCH Statements

Check if _____ has _____ before _____ .

EXAMPLE

answer = input("What is 5 - 7?")

....

....
print("Correct!")

....
print("Forgot minus sign?")

....
print("Wrong!")

....

The _____ of 'answer' determines which _____ to use.

Each _____ should be _____ to the same place.

SWITCH only checks ....
................., not ....
like IF-ELSEIF.

_____ comes at the end and used if _____ .

Iteration

FOR Loops

Repeat code a _____ number of times. Number of repeats depends on
_____, _____, and _____ (optional).

Code to repeat is
indented between
'_____' and '_____'.

```
for k = 1 to 15 step 2
    print(k)
next k
```

Counts up in steps of _____.
Default step count is _____.

The counter variable can be used inside the loop.

FOR loops are
........-controlled.

DO UNTIL Loops

Repeats until a
condition is _____.

Condition checked at
_____ of loop.

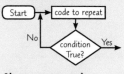

Always runs code
_____.

Infinite loop if condition
always _____.

EXAMPLE

Write code for a dart game that counts down
from 301. Stop when the player reaches 0.
If they go under 0, ask them to throw again.

Using DO UNTIL:

```
score = 301

........
    throw = input("Enter throw:")
    if ..................................... then
        print("Throw again")
    else

        ...........................................
    endif
    print(str(score) + " left")
.................................
```

WHILE Loops

Repeats while a
condition is _____.

Condition checked at
_____ of loop.

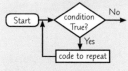

Never runs code if
condition is _____.

Infinite loop if condition
always _____.

Using WHILE:

These two loops are
...................-controlled.

```
score = 301
.................................
    throw = input("Enter throw:")
    if ..................................... then
        print("Throw again")
    else

        ...........................................
    endif
    print(str(score) + " left")
.................................
```

Second Go: ..... /..... /.....	**Iteration**

FOR Loops

Repeat code [_____] . Number of repeats depends
on [_____] , and [_____] (optional).

Code to repeat is
indented between
'[____]' and '[____]'.

```
.......... k = 1 ...... 15 ........... 2 ◄ Counts up in [_____] .
     print(k)                           Default step count is [__] .
.............. k
```

The [_____] can be used inside the loop.

FOR loops are
....

DO UNTIL Loops

Repeats [_____]

Condition
at [_____] .

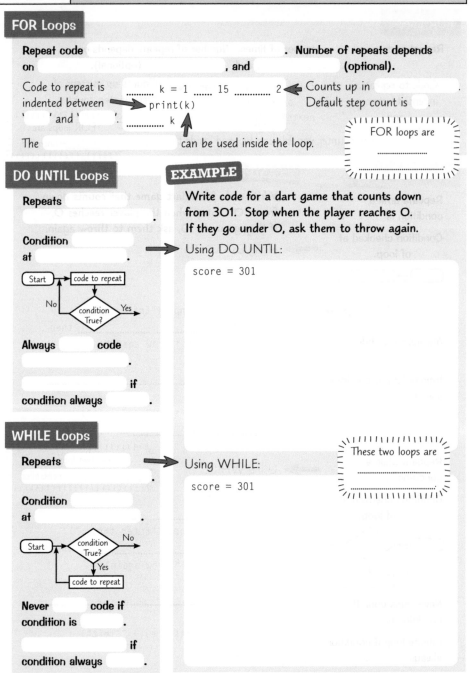

Start → code to repeat

No / condition True? / Yes

Always [____] code
[_____] .

[_____] if
condition always [____] .

WHILE Loops

Repeats [_____]
[_____] .

Condition
at [_____] .

Start → condition True? → No
↓ Yes
code to repeat

Never [____] code if
condition is [____] .

[_____] if
condition always [____] .

EXAMPLE

Write code for a dart game that counts down
from 301. Stop when the player reaches 0.
If they go under 0, ask them to throw again.

Using DO UNTIL:

```
score = 301
```

Using WHILE:

```
score = 301
```

These two loops are
....

 ☑ ☑ ☑

Checking Multiple Conditions

Nested Selection Statements

Make another selection depending on the .... of a previous ....

EXAMPLE

Write an algorithm that checks a user's age. If they're under 9,
ask them to multiply their age by 7 and check their answer.
Print a different message for each possible outcome.

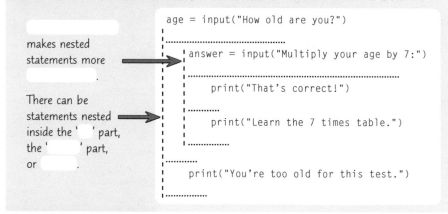

_____ makes nested
statements more _____ .

There can be
statements nested
inside the ' ___ ' part,
the ' _____ ' part,
or _____ .

```
age = input("How old are you?")
...............................
answer = input("Multiply your age by 7:")
...............................
    print("That's correct!")
............
    print("Learn the 7 times table.")
.............
    print("You're too old for this test.")
.............
```

Using Boolean Operators

Boolean operators can be used in .... and .... statements
to .... more than one .... at once.

EXAMPLE

Use a while loop to give 3 attempts to enter one of two valid passwords
("Meg123" or "Adm1n!"). Once a valid password is entered, set 'access'
to True and exit the loop, otherwise 'access' should be False.

```
attempts = 0
access = False
..............................................................
    pw = input("Password:")
    attempts = ...............................
    if ................................................................ then
        access = ...............
    endif
..............................
```

Repeat while
fewer than
3 attempts
have been
made, and
while 'access'
is False.

Check both
passwords
in a single
IF statement
condition.

Checking Multiple Conditions

Nested Selection Statements

Make .... depending on the .... of a .... selection.

> **EXAMPLE**
>
> Write an algorithm that checks a user's age. If they're under 9,
> ask them to multiply their age by 7 and check their answer.
> Print a different message for each possible outcome.
>
> ```
> age = input("How old are you?")
> if age < 9 then
>     answer = input("Multiply your age by 7:")
> ```

Using Boolean Operators

Boolean operators can be used in ....
to ....

> **EXAMPLE**
>
> Use a while loop to give 3 attempts to enter one of two valid passwords
> ("Meg123" or "Adm1n!"). Once a valid password is entered, set 'access'
> to True and exit the loop, otherwise 'access' should be False.
>
> ```
> attempts = 0
> access = False
> ```

Mixed Practice Quizzes

If you've mastered the topics on pages 87-92, then have a go at these quizzes.
Else go back over the content until you feel fully prepared. Endif...

Quiz 1   Date: ...... / ...... / ......

1) True or false? Comparison operators and Boolean operators can be used in **IF** statement conditions.

2) Explain the purpose of the default case in a **SWITCH** statement.

3) What type of construct is an **IF** statement — selection or iteration?

4) Which iteration statement checks its condition at the start of each loop?

5) In what scenario would a **DO UNTIL** loop repeat infinitely?

6) True or false? The 'else' part of an **IF** statement is optional.

7) Outline how a **SWITCH** statement works.

8) Sketch a flowchart for a **DO UNTIL** loop.

9) What is the purpose of the 'step' command in a **FOR** loop?

10)* Write an algorithm using a **WHILE** loop to print the characters of "spaceship" one at a time.

Total:

Quiz 2   Date: ...... / ...... / ......

1) Name one example of a condition-controlled loop.

2) True or false? An **IF-ELSEIF** statement can include an 'else' part.

3) In what scenario would a **WHILE** loop repeat infinitely?

4) True or false? Selection statements can be nested inside each other.

5) Give one reason for using indentation in program code.

6) What type of construct is a **SWITCH** statement — selection or iteration?

7) Why might you use the **AND** operator in a **WHILE** loop condition?

8) Sketch a flowchart for an **IF** statement.

9) Give one reason for using a **DO UNTIL** loop instead of a **WHILE** loop.

10)* Describe the output of the following code:
```
for k = 1 to 99 step 2
    print(k)
next k
```

Total:

Mixed Practice Quizzes

Quiz 3

Date: ...... / ...... / ......

1) Give one reason for using a **WHILE** loop over a **DO UNTIL** loop.

2) Explain the purpose of the 'else' part of an **IF** statement.

3) Give two values that must be specified in a **FOR** loop statement.

4) True or false? An **IF** statement can only be nested within the 'else' part of another **IF** statement.

5) What type of construct is a **DO UNTIL** statement — selection or iteration?

6) Why might you use the **OR** operator in an **IF** statement condition?

7) Which iteration statement always runs a fixed number of times?

8) Sketch a flowchart for a **WHILE** loop.

9) Give one reason for using an **IF-ELSEIF** statement over a **SWITCH** statement.

10)* Write an algorithm using a **FOR** loop to print the first 20 cube numbers.

Total:

Quiz 4

Date: ...... / ...... / ......

1) What keyword always comes at the end of a **FOR** loop?

2) Outline how an **IF-ELSEIF** statement works.

3) Which iteration statement checks its condition at the end of each loop, **WHILE** or **DO UNTIL**?

4) In what scenario would a **WHILE** loop never run the code inside it?

5) Why are nested **IF** statements useful?

6)* Write an algorithm using a **DO UNTIL** loop to add consecutive integers starting at 1 until the total exceeds 1000.

7) True or false? A **SWITCH** statement can check the values of multiple variables.

8) Explain how a **FOR** loop is different to a **WHILE** loop.

9)* Sketch a flowchart for a **SWITCH** statement with three cases.

10)* In the following **IF** statement condition, identify one integer value of x that returns True and one that returns False: 'if x < 50 AND x > 45 then'.

Total:

Arrays

Purpose of Arrays

ARRAY — a data structure that stores a _____ of values with the same _____ .

- Each value is called an _____ .
- _____ are accessed by position (index), starting at position ⬚ .

One-Dimensional Arrays

A 1D array is like a ⬚ .

You can either create arrays by setting their ⬚ , then assigning ⬚ ...

```
............. friends........
friends........ = "Abi"
friends........ = "Ben"
friends........ = "Cho"
```

⬅ Can contain 3 elements (at positions _____).

... or do it in one step by giving _____ :

```
............. friends = ["Abi", "Ben", "Cho"]
```

Retrieve elements by _____ . Change elements by _____ new values.

```
print(friends........)
```
```
Abi
```

_____ = "Bilal" ⬅

Replaces element at position ⬚ ("Ben") with "Bilal".

Two-Dimensional Arrays

A 2D array is like a .... You can also think of them as a 1D array where each element is a ....

Positions of elements are written like .... or ....

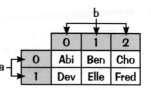

	b		
	0	1	2
a 0	Abi	Ben	Cho
1	Dev	Elle	Fred

EXAMPLE

The 2D array 'runs' is used to store the number of runs scored by two cricketers in their last four matches. E.g. runs[2, 0] returns 65.

Write an algorithm to set all values in the array back to 0.

The i FOR loop goes ➡ through the 4 rows.

The j FOR loop goes through the 2 columns.

```
for i = .............
  for j = .............
    ............. = 0
  next j
next i
```

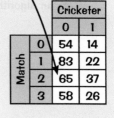

		Cricketer	
		0	1
Match	0	54	14
	1	83	22
	2	65	37
	3	58	26

Arrays

Purpose of Arrays

ARRAY — [blank]

- Each value is called an [blank].
- [blank] are accessed by [blank] (index), starting at [blank].

One-Dimensional Arrays

A 1D array is like a [blank]. You can either create arrays by [blank] ...

.... friends........ ⬅ Can contain 3 [blank] (at positions [blank]).

.... = "Abi"   ... or do it in one step by [blank]:

.... = "Ben"   .... friends = ...

.... = "Cho"

Retrieve elements by [blank].   Change elements by [blank].

print(.............................)   .... ⬅

Abi   Replaces element at position [blank] ("Ben") with "Bilal".

Two-Dimensional Arrays

A 2D array is like a .... You can also think of them as
a .... where each element is a ....
Positions of elements are written like .... or ....

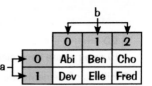

	0	1	2
0	Abi	Ben	Cho
1	Dev	Elle	Fred

b (across top), a (down left)

EXAMPLE

The 2D array 'runs' is used to store the number of runs scored by
two cricketers in their last four matches. E.g. runs[2, 0] returns 65.

Write an algorithm to set all values in the array back to 0.

	Cricketer	
	0	1
Match 0	54	14
1	83	22
2	65	37
3	58	26

File Handling

External Files

Allow programs to .... data that's not written directly in the ....
Can .... data so that it's not .... when a program is closed.

Six File Operations

① `newFile("myFile.txt")`

.... a new file with the given .... (or ....).

② `file = open("myFile.txt")`

.... a file — the file needs to be assigned to a variable.

These commands are called on the variable that stores the file.

③ `file.readLine()`

Returns the .... of the file, starting from the beginning.

After this command, the file 'cursor' moves to the beginning of the next line.

④ `file.writeLine("text")`

Writes a .... at the .... of the file.

⑤ `file.endOfFile()`

Returns .... if the 'cursor' is at the end of the file, otherwise ....

⑥ `file.close()`

.... the file allowing other users to access the updated file.

EXAMPLE

Karim's shopping list is stored in an array called 'list'. The variable 'n' stores the number of items in the list.

```
list = ["eggs", "bread", "milk"]
n = 3
```

a) Write an algorithm to save the list to an external file.

```
filename = "shopping.txt"
.....................(filename)
shopList = .............(filename)
for i = 0 to .............
    shopList.............................(list[i])
next i
shopList.....................
```

The file will look like this. →

eggs
bread
milk

b) Write an algorithm to output every line from the file "stock.txt" so Karim can check which items the shop has.

```
stock = .............("stock.txt")
while NOT stock.................................
    line = stock...............................
    print(line)
endwhile
stock.....................
```

Second Go: ..... /..... /.....	**File Handling**

External Files

Allow programs to _____ that's not written _____ .

Can _____ data so that it's not _____ .

Six File Operations

1 `newFile("myFile.txt")`

2 `file = open("myFile.txt")`

3 `file.readLine()`

4 `file.writeLine("text")`

5 `file.endOfFile()`

6 `file.close()`

Karim's shopping list is stored in an array called 'list'. The variable 'n' stores the number of items in the list.

```
list = ["eggs", "bread", "milk"]
n = 3
```

a) Write an algorithm to save the list to an external file.

```
filename = "shopping.txt"
```

The file will look like this. ➡

eggs bread milk

b) Write an algorithm to output every line from the file "stock.txt" so Karim can check which items the shop has.

```
stock = open("stock.txt")
```

Storing and Searching Data

Records

RECORD — a data structure that stores related [____] of different data types.

FIELD — an [____] of a [____] used to store one piece of data.

Create a fixed record structure by giving a [____] and [____] for each field.

```
record ticket
    string filmName
    int seatNumber
    real price
endrecord
```

Create records by giving [____] for each field:

```
ticket1 = ticket("Data Force", 16, 7.50)
```

Use the [____] and [____] name to access values:

```
print(.....................·.....................)
```
➡ | 16 |

You can use [____] to group records with the same structure together.

SQL

Structured Query Language (SQL) is used to [____], [____], [____] and maintain database tables.

Each row is a [____]. ➡

The columns are [____].

Table: cars

ID	regNum	year	price	fuel
1	JZ23 IQZ	2023	24000	Petrol
2	XJ18 QSI	2018	8999	Diesel
3	IQ21 UIK	2021	12500	Petrol

SELECT and FROM

Statements to specify which [____] to return from which [____].

```
SELECT * FROM cars
```

Use this character to return [____] ...

```
SELECT regNum FROM cars
```

...or [____] which [____] to return from each record.

➡

regNum
JZ23 IQZ
XJ18 QSI
IQ21 UIK

WHERE

A statement to specify .... that a .... should satisfy before being returned. Use Boolean operators to check .... conditions.

EXAMPLE

Write a search query to return the year and price of all cars with price less than 20000 and fuel not equal to "Diesel".

```
.................. year, price ............ cars
.................. price < 20000 ......... fuel != "Diesel"
```

➡

year	price
2021	12500

Storing and Searching Data

Records

RECORD —

FIELD —

Create a fixed record structure by giving _____ for each field.

.... ticket
    string filmName
    int seatNumber
    real price
....

Create records by giving _____:

    ticket1 = ticket("Data Force", 16, 7.50)

Use the _____ name to access values:

    print(..................... . ...) ➡ 16

You can use _____ to group records with _____ together.

SQL

Structured Query Language (SQL) is used to

The columns are _____ .

Table: cars

ID	regNum	year	price	fuel
1	JZ23 IQZ	2023	24000	Petrol
2	XJ18 QSI	2018	8999	Diesel
3	IQ21 UIK	2021	12500	Petrol

Each row is a _____ . ➡

SELECT and FROM

Statements to specify _____ .

    SELECT .... FROM cars   _____

regNum
JZ23 IQZ
XJ18 QSI
IQ21 UIK

Use this character to return _____ ...

...or _____ which _____ to return from each record.

WHERE

A statement to ....
before being returned. Use .... operators to .... conditions.

EXAMPLE

Write a search query to return the year and price of all cars with price less than 20000 and fuel not equal to "Diesel".

year	price
....	....

Sub Programs

Key Definitions

SUB PROGRAM	A set of .... stored under one name that are .... when called. They help to improve code ...., improve .... and avoid .... code.
PARAMETER	A .... used to pass .... into a sub program. Can be any .... (e.g. integer, string, array, etc.).
ARGUMENT	The value a .... takes when a sub program is called.
LOCAL VARIABLE	Can only be used within the structure they're .... in.
GLOBAL VARIABLE	.... with the keyword '...............'. Can be used any time after ...., in any part of the program.

Procedures

PROCEDURE — a sub program that doesn't ....

EXAMPLE

Sub programs are declared with a .... and .... in brackets.

Call a procedure using its .... Give any .... in brackets.

```
procedure printSquare(number)
    print(number * number)
endprocedure
printSquare(5)
```

```
25
```

Functions

FUNCTION — a sub program that does ....

EXAMPLE

Write a function to reverse a string. Show it working on the string "!elloH".

All variables inside the function are .... variables.

Store returned values to use them later in the program.

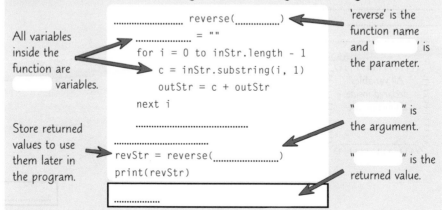

```
.................. reverse(............)
    .............. = ""
    for i = 0 to inStr.length - 1
        c = inStr.substring(i, 1)
        outStr = c + outStr
    next i

    ...................................
    ...................................
revStr = reverse(..................)
print(revStr)
```

```
..................
```

'reverse' is the function name and '........' is the parameter.

"........" is the argument.

"........" is the returned value.

 ☑ ☑ ☑

Second Go: ..... /..... /.....	**Sub Programs**

Key Definitions

SUB PROGRAM	They help to improve .
PARAMETER	Can be any (e.g. , array, etc.).
ARGUMENT	The value a
LOCAL VARIABLE	Can only be used
GLOBAL VARIABLE	Declared with the keyword ' '. Can be used

Procedures

PROCEDURE — ....
....

EXAMPLE

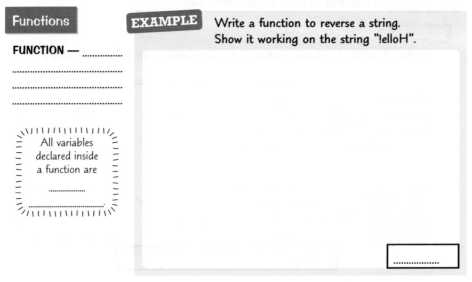

Sub programs are declared with a .... ➡ .... printSquare(number)
and .... in ....:   print(number * number)

.... a procedure using its ....: ➡ ....
Give any .... in ....: printSquare(5)   ....

Functions

EXAMPLE

FUNCTION — ....
....
....
....

Write a function to reverse a string.
Show it working on the string "!elloH".

\\||||||||||||||//
All variables
declared inside
a function are

....
//||||||||||||||\\

....

 ☑ ☑ ☑

Mixed Practice Quizzes

Here are the last set of quizzes for this section. You'll need the following query:
SELECT info FROM pages WHERE pageNum >= 95 AND pageNum <= 102.

Quiz 1 Date: ...... / ...... / ......

1) What is an array?
2) Define the term 'field' (in relation to a record).
3) Why are external files used when programming?
4) What does SQL stand for?
5)* What's wrong with the following code? array data = [123, "abc"]
6) Briefly describe how the readLine() function works.
7) Explain how sub programs can improve code.
8) True or false? A record structure can change after it has been defined.
9) What should immediately follow 'SELECT' in an SQL query?
10) Define the term 'local variable'.

Total:

Quiz 2 Date: ...... / ...... / ......

1)* array sizes = [3, 4, 5]. What is the value of sizes[2]?
2) What argument must be given to the open() file handling function?
3) What two things need to be specified when defining a field in a record?
4) True or false? An SQL query can return more than one field.
5) What is the difference between an argument and a parameter?
6) What is a two dimensional array?
7) Explain the purpose of the endOfFile() function.
8) Name two types of sub program.
9)* What is missing from the following line of code?
   function (name, age, height)
10) Explain the purpose of the WHERE command in an SQL query.

Total:

Mixed Practice Quizzes

Quiz 3 Date: ...... / ...... / ......

1) Describe two ways that an array can be created.
2) What is the purpose of the function newFile()?
3) Describe one key difference between arrays and records.
4) Give two things that SQL can be used to do with a database.
5) What is a procedure?
6)* 'score' is an array. What does the following code do? score[0] = 7
7)* Explain what the following line of code will do: file.writeLine("GoodBye")
8) True or false? All sub programs have at least two parameters.
9) What should immediately follow 'FROM' in an SQL query?
10) Define the term 'global variable'. How are they declared?

Total:

Quiz 4 Date: ...... / ...... / ......

1) What is a function?
2) How is an element of a two dimensional array accessed?
3)* What is wrong with the following line of code? open("myFile.text")
4) True or false? A parameter of a procedure could be an array.
5)* A variable 'person' stores a record with a field called 'name'.
    Write a line of code to change the value of this field to "Kolo".
6) What character can be used to return all fields in an SQL query?
7) State one problem that may arise if the close() file handling function
    is not used after making changes to a file.
8) True or false? Arrays can group records with the same structure together.
9)* Write an SQL query to return the field 'name' from the table 'people'.
10)* Write a function that returns the percentage discount
    when given an initial price and sale price.

Total:

Structured Programming

First Go:
..... /..... /.....

Using Structure Diagrams

STRUCTURE DIAGRAM — a tool you can use to help
_____ and _____ programs.

1 _____ the program into manageable _____.

2 Continue _____ into smaller _____, until each one performs a _____.

3 Write _____ to carry out each _____.

4 Build the bigger _____ and main program from the _____.

EXAMPLE

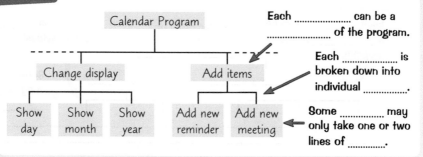

Calendar Program

Change display   Add items

Show day | Show month | Show year   Add new reminder | Add new meeting

Each _____ can be a _____ of the program.

Each _____ is broken down into individual _____.

Some _____ may only take one or two lines of _____.

The advantage of using structure diagrams is that modules can be...

_____ independently   _____ individually   _____ elsewhere

Four Ways to Improve Maintainability

Well-maintained code is _____ for other programmers to _____.
They can _____ parts of the code without causing _____ elsewhere.

1 Write _____ to explain what code does.

2 Use _____ to make program flow clear to see.

3 Use descriptive _____ for variables, sub programs and parameters so it's easier to _____.

4 Use _____ to separate parts of the program.

_____ are usually written after //.

 ✓   ✓   ✓

Second Go: ...... /...... /......	**Structured Programming**

Using Structure Diagrams

STRUCTURE DIAGRAM — ....

....

1. .... the program into ....
2. Continue .... until ....
3. Write ....
4. Build ....

EXAMPLE

Each .... can be a .... of the program.

Calendar Program

Each .... is .... into individual ....

Some .... may only take

....

....

The advantage of using structure diagrams is that modules can be...

Four Ways to Improve Maintainability

Well-maintained code is .... for other programmers to .... They can .... without ....

.... are usually written after ....

1. Write ....
2. ....
3. ....
4. ....

Defensive Design

Robust Programming

Programs that function correctly shouldn't .... or produce ....

Avoid these problems by using defensive design:

Anticipate and prevent .... by users.

Keep code ....

Reduce errors by ....

Five Validation Checks

INPUT VALIDATION — checking if data meets ....
before passing it into a program.

Programs often use a mixture of validation checks, including:

Validation check	What it does...
1 Range check	Checks the data is ....
2 Presence check	Checks the data has ....
3 Format check	Checks the data has .... , e.g. a date.
4 Look-up table	Checks the data against a table of ....
5 Length check	Checks the data is ....

Authentication

AUTHENTICATION — confirming the .... of a user before allowing ....

.... or biometrics are usually associated with a username.

Four ways to make passwords more secure:

1 Force strong passwords — long with a mix of .... , ... and ....

2 Limit the number of .... authentication attempts.

3 Require that passwords are .... regularly.

4 Ask for a .... selection of .... from a password on each attempt.

Section Seven — Design, Testing and IDEs

| Second Go: ...... /...... /...... | **Defensive Design** |

Robust Programming

Programs that function correctly shouldn't ....

Avoid these problems by using defensive design:

| Anticipate | Keep | Reduce |

Five Validation Checks

INPUT VALIDATION — ....
....

Programs often use a mixture of validation checks, including:

Validation check	What it does...
①	
②	
③	
④	
⑤	

Authentication

AUTHENTICATION — ....
....

.... or .... are usually associated with a ....

Four ways to make passwords more secure:

①	Force
②	Limit
③	Require
④	Ask for

Section Seven — Design, Testing and IDEs

Errors and Trace Tables

Two Types of Error

1 **SYNTAX ERROR** — when the ....
of the programming language have been ....

2 **LOGIC ERROR** — when a program is able to ....
but does something ....

Translators can find .... errors, but they won't pick up .... errors.

EXAMPLE

This function should check
if a number is in a range.
Identify the syntax and logic errors.

```
function inRange(n, min, max
    if n > min OR n < max then
        return True
    else
        return False
    endif
endfunction
```

Syntax error: In line ......, there is a ....
.... missing at ....

Logic error: In line ......, the .... won't always lead to the desired
outcome — both conditions need to be .... to get the correct result,
so the .... should be used there instead.

Trace Tables

Trace tables keep track of the .... certain
.... take as a program ....

Columns could also represent other things, e.g. lengths of arrays.

- Columns usually represent ....
- Rows show .... at a particular point.

They can be used to check for .... errors or to work out what a program is doing.

EXAMPLE

Complete the trace table when the algorithm below is run.
Explain what the algorithm does.

```
a = 2
b = 3
c = 0
for i = 1 to b
    c = c + a
next i
print(c)
```

i	a	b	c
—	2	3	0
	2	3	
	2	3	
	2	3	

← Each .... has a column.

← Values before the ....

← .... is added to .... each time .... increases.

← Last value of .... is output.

The algorithm calculates .... and outputs the result.

Section Seven — Design, Testing and IDEs

Errors and Trace Tables

Two Types of Error

1 SYNTAX ERROR — ....

....

....

2 LOGIC ERROR — ....

....

Translators can find .... errors, but they won't pick up .... errors.

EXAMPLE

This function should check if a number is in a range.

Identify the syntax and logic errors.

```
function inRange(n, min, max
    if n > min OR n < max then
        return True
    else
        return False
    endif
endfunction
```

Syntax error:

Logic error:

Trace Tables

Trace tables ....

....

• Columns usually represent ....

• Rows show ....

They can be used to check for .... or ....

....

Columns could also represent other things, e.g. ....

EXAMPLE

Complete the trace table when the algorithm below is run.
Explain what the algorithm does.

```
a = 2
b = 3
c = 0
for i = 1 to b
    c = c + a
next i
print(c)
```

⬅ Each .... has a column.

⬅ Values before the ....

⬅ ..... is .... each time ....

⬅ Last value of ..... is output.

The algorithm ....

Testing

Two Types of Testing

Testing can happen at different points in .... :

1. **ITERATIVE TESTING** — testing a program .... it's being ....
   - Individual .... can be tested and .... fixed.
   - Process is .... until modules ....
   - Fixing small .... early prevents large .... later on.

2. **FINAL TESTING** — testing a program at the ....
   - The whole .... is tested at the ....
   - Check for .... where modules .... with each other.

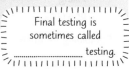

Final testing is sometimes called .... testing.

Combining iterative and final testing helps .... errors.

Four Types of Test Data

TEST PLAN — a detailed plan of how a .... is going to be .... , including what .... will be used.

TEST DATA — .... chosen to see if a .... is working properly.

1. **NORMAL DATA** — .... users are .... to enter.

2. **BOUNDARY DATA** — values at the .... of what the program will ....

3. **INVALID DATA** — has .... data type but should be ....

4. **ERRONEOUS DATA** — has .... data type and should be ....

EXAMPLE Complete this test plan for setting a digital thermostat. It should accept temperatures in the range 5-30 °C.

Type	Test data	Reason for testing	Expected outcome
Normal	12	Check	Temperature ....
Boundary	30	Check the .... value.	Temperature ....
Invalid	2	Check values that are too	Error: ....
Erroneous	"1X"	Check	Error: ....

Section Seven — Design, Testing and IDEs

| Second Go: ..... / ..... / ..... | **Testing** |

Two Types of Testing

Testing can happen at different points in ....:

① **ITERATIVE TESTING —**

* Individual

* Process is

* Fixing prevents

② **FINAL TESTING —**

* The whole

* Check for errors where

Combining iterative and final testing helps .... errors.

Final testing is sometimes called .... testing.

Four Types of Test Data

TEST PLAN — ....
....
....
....

TEST DATA — ....
....
....
....

① **NORMAL DATA —**

② **BOUNDARY DATA —**

③ **INVALID DATA —**

④ **ERRONEOUS DATA —**

EXAMPLE Complete this test plan for setting a digital thermostat. It should accept temperatures in the range 5-30 °C.

Type	Test Data	Reason for testing	Expected outcome
	12	Check	
		Check the largest value.	
	2	Check	
	"1X"	Check	

Languages, Translators & IDEs

High-Level Languages

The majority of code is written in high-level languages, e.g. ....

- One instruction represents many instructions of .... code.
- Same code works on .... machines or processors.
- Code is .... to read and write.
- Don't need to know about the .... or .... structure.
- Must be translated or interpreted before it can be ....
- .... and less .... efficient.

Low-Level Languages

.... code → 00000 00010 00011...

.... languages → ADD r4, r2, r3

- One instruction of .... code can represent one of .... code.
- Code usually only works for .... machine or processor.
- Code is .... to read and write.
- Need to know internal structure of .... and how it manages ....
- .... code can be .... directly, without being ....
- .... and more .... efficient.

Compilers

- Translates all code at once into .... code, creating an ....
- Only needed for initial ....
- Returns a list of .... for whole program when compiling is ....
- Compiling can take ...., but program runs .... once compiled.

Interpreters

- Translates and .... one .... at a time using its own .... code subroutines.
- Used every time code is ....
- Stops and returns .... error found.
- Programs run more ....

Five Features of IDEs

INTEGRATED DEVELOPMENT ENVIRONMENT (IDE) —

....

① Code editor	Where .... Can often automatically ...., ..., ... and .... code.	
② Run-time environment	Allows code to be .... and .... within the IDE.	
③ Error diagnostics	Debugging tool to show information about detected	
④ Breakpoints	.... the program at certain lines. .... can be checked to help diagnose .... errors.	
⑤	A compiler or interpreter to allow source code to be executed.	

Languages, Translators & IDEs

High-Level Languages

The majority of code is written in high-level languages, e.g. ....

- One instruction represents ____ instructions of ____.
- Same code works on ____.
- Code is ____ to ____.
- Don't need to know about the ____.
- Must be ____ before it can be ____.
- ____ and less ____ efficient.

Low-Level Languages

.... code ➜ 00000 00010 00011...
.... languages ➜ ADD r4, r2, r3

- One instruction of ____ can represent one of ____.
- Code usually only works for ____.
- Code is ____ to ____.
- Need to know ____ and how it ____.
- ____ code can be ____ directly, without being ____.
- ____ and more ____ efficient.

Compilers

- Translates all ____, creating ____.
- Needed once for ____.
- Returns ____ for ____ when compiling is ____.
- Compiling can ____, but program runs ____.

Interpreters

- Translates and ____ using its own ____.
- Used every time ____.
- Stops and returns ____.
- Programs run ____.

Five Features of IDEs

INTEGRATED DEVELOPMENT ENVIRONMENT (IDE) — ....

①	Code editor	
②	Run-time environment	
③	Error diagnostics	
④	Breakpoints	
⑤	Translator	

Mixed Practice Quizzes

Testing, testing. Ah, there we go, some more quizzes for you. See what you can remember from p.105-114, then check you haven't made any logic errors.

Quiz 1   Date: ...... / ...... / ......

1) Name two types of translator and describe how they work.
2) What is a syntax error?
3) What are IDEs used for?
4) What type of testing involves repeatedly testing a program during development?
5) Why should descriptive names be used in code?
6) List three types of input validation check.
7) What is a trace table?
8) Give four ways that passwords can be made more secure.
9)* Which of these is an example of invalid test data for a digital clock?
   12:00   11:62   00:00   CR:07
10) Give two reasons why code should be well-maintained.

Total:

Quiz 2   Date: ...... / ...... / ......

1) What is a structure diagram?
2) What is a test plan, and what does it include?
3) Give three differences between compilers and interpreters.
4) Which feature of IDEs pauses the program at a specified line of code?
5) What is a logic error?
6) How do sub programs improve code maintainability?
7) List three things that can be done to make robust programs using defensive design.
8) Give two examples of low-level languages.
9) Which type of error can be picked up by translators: syntax or logic?
10) What is the difference between iterative and final testing?

Total:

Mixed Practice Quizzes

Quiz 3   Date: ...... / ...... / ......

1) How are comments usually denoted in code?
2) Define the term 'input validation'.
3) How is decomposition used in structured programming?
4) Why are trace tables useful?
5) True or false? High-level languages only work on one machine or processor.
6) Give three benefits of using iterative testing.
7) What is a range check?
8) Give two things that columns could represent in trace tables.
9) True or false? You can combine iterative and final testing for the same program.
10) Which validation check makes sure that data has actually been entered?

Total:

Quiz 4   Date: ...... / ...... / ......

1) Name the four types of test data.
2) Give two reasons why final testing is useful.
3) Give three benefits of breaking a program into modules.
4) What is the purpose of the error diagnostic feature of an IDE?
5) What is meant by authentication? Give two ways this could be done.
6) List four ways to improve the maintainability of code.
7) What do rows show in a trace table?
8)* Identify the syntax error: print("hello world)
9) What makes a password strong?
10) Give three differences between low-level and high-level languages.

Total: